BUIL

UNIVER

CATE TROWBRIDGE LISI

Max, the Mini, and one Tuscan summer

www.europebooks.co.uk | info@europebooks.co.uk

ISBN 9791220134125
First edition: January 2023

Edited by Stella Fusca

Max, the Mini, and one Tuscan Summer

To my lovely girls,

and the only long suffering male in the family - Max.

Sometimes a poor dogs' lot
can just be a little too much to bear …

INDEX

Introduction

Max Puttanus Troius!

This was the adoptive kennel name on behalf of the Lisi family, for this handsome 3-year-old terrier, a curious, random blend of Jack Russell, with a smidge of shih-tzu, and extremely possibly, a lot of fox. Hence his pale russet colour, white bib, and penchant for chasing to little avail, his feral cousins across the hidden folds of east Sussex fields. Acutely sensitive, and with the classic JRT intelligence, the following account describes one summer in Tuscany, following, very loosely, the style of Virginia Woolf's Flush. Our family's travels, as seen through Max's eyes.

Chapter One: Max joins the Lisi family

The car, as a general rule, was not exactly a love of mine, having had no experience, outside of fleeting visions of seeing dismayed and confused faces of my kin, leaving the farm. One of my first memories served to alienate its use and presence, entirely.

At Only a few months, sitting comfortably in the lap of my "padroncina", Isabella, a lively 10 year old at the time, my paws splayed, on the dashboard, head up inquisitively, my attention, occasionally and casually straying to dogs on leads with their owners on the passing pavements, to whom I would, in general, excitedly bark in recognition, raising myself up on my hind paws, in the attempt to gain attention, as we pootered gently past.

Then, one fine spring day, my vehicle experience was indelibly changed. On a nearby trip down to Rye harbour, habitually a treat and all-round enjoyable experience for me. I recognised every roundabout and steeple, with renewed excitement every morning, or afternoon.

I strained on my lead painfully, in anticipation, each rancid puddle and steaming pile of poo was mine to explore and examine with the deepest of intensity, on arrival there.

On this occasion however, pending the all-important turn off, we were surrounded by a huge rumbling and deafening roar of a group of mustachioed motorcyclists accelerating, in the attempt to overtake us. The searing explosion, crushing brutally, my former innocent puppyish peace and calm. I deepened my claws, primed- my senses, panicked. I excitedly leapt up and down on Isabella's lap, outraged, fuming, my protective instincts to the fore, barking loudly and repetitively.

The assault on my sensitive ears, both from this explosive and deeply threatening roar, combined with Isabella and Mamma C, swearing loudly in Italian, “Zitto ... ma basta ... è possibile?”, to quieten me, traumatised me so much so, that, from that moment, my only safe place in the car... of any type... and this included also trains, which I found even more terrifying, was to resolve my extreme discomfort by coiling myself tightly, and squishing myself as tightly to the car floor as was doggily possible ,,, and then.. on occasion farting silently (well mostly) from beneath the seat, coiled around in my tight ball, eyes obliviously shutting out the world.

Just a couple of weeks previously, I had been “plucked”, as a 3-month-old, or thereabouts, a happy little mutt, from my "woodlands " farm, somewhere off the beaten track in High

Halden, in the wild country between Ashford and Tenterden.

My bed had been an old horsehair cushion in a draughty barn that I shared with my most convivial of aunties, A congenial leggy, tufty, extremely wily creature, who had taught me the most important tools for a high-born gypsy dog.

I would bark myself practically dizzy, whilst chasing at top speed, the many and varied trailers that came up and down the track, dodging the wheels skilfully, as the men driving would holler and swear from the truck windows.

Befriending, sometimes, the formerly spirited (as some of them seemed) and ever-changing horses that seemed too sad, when they were physically hauled, their shoes squealing on the stepped ledges up to the boxes that stenched of death, away to some unknown place.

My sense of smell, thereby, had already developed excellently, so as to sniff out the tiniest of sausage or bacon morsels in the full to bursting black bin bags, left, under the trees, haphazardly, in the entrance to the farm. Which I discovered by gently piercing with my razor-sharp teeth, I could scatter with the most accomplished technique, the contents distinguishing the greasiest bacon rinds, mouldering chunks of cheese and discarded lumps of half chewed rotting meat.

An achievement that I found hard to accept, when caught by the otherwise almost obsolete owners of the farm, was rewarded with a boot up the bum, and harsh words.
How could the humans be so strangely ignorant? These were talents to be admired and cherished, surely??!
I fancied myself quite the macho, hardy type, already capable of outwitting even the fastest of the runners on the farm, having dodged and fled, the sweatiest and most aggressive of the farmers' sons, albeit still a pup.
I was confident in my being able to take care of myself and was enjoying my newfound solitude. My one remaining companion, the friendly white and ginger curly tufted aunty, Toots.
My numerous brothers and sisters, with whom I had cut my teeth, and had slept tightly bunched together in the shed, had all been taken by various smiling and simpering families, in the last week: and my dear mama, teets still dragging almost the sawdust in the shed, thought to be newly in pup, had been moved to alternative suitable accommodation.
And so, one bright morning, in an old faded green tinpot of a car, my family arrived. In the back, gazing out in rapt anticipation, 2 beautiful little angels, one on the cusp of puberty, and with a hesitation that was almost palpable, the other still a child with such excitement, she was unable to

contain it- her dream, finally being realised. All of those infant years, leaving baby milk teeth for the tooth fairy, gazing up at the new moons in Italy, wishing and hoping.
I did my best to appear completely irresistible, sensing an underlying sadness in both children, and the Mamma too. They were certainly loving, BUT....... Toots advised me well, I was the last puppy of the litter, and not a popular addition to the farm, the farmer, who I had only seen briefly, and mostly only by his boot, had unimaginatively named me "spot". Which was a strange thing, as I strongly remembered each of my siblings, all leaving the farm, with the exact same name.
The family didn't stand a chance- I was destined for them. There was an older lady, with the group, and by far, she was the wisest, not at all convinced by the surroundings, or indeed by my infinite charms, as I yipped playfully, and played the subdued and affectionate pup, welcoming the girls' cuddles and kisses. The children, my saviour angels, begged and pleaded. Unconvinced, but acquiescing to their pleas, she signed a cheque duly away in the farmhouse, and I was loaded into the old tinpot of a car, and returned home with them to Rye, to become the latest member of the Lisi family.

Settling into my new family life, was .... terribly traumatic-
I missed my old freedom of the barn, the tractor and trailer chasing, the horses coming and going, the frequent shouting and yelling at my antics.
I now had the run of a big, clapboarded house, with a wonderful grassy garden, soft under my paws, with the biggest copper beech and laelandai trees, that were a joy to sniff and rub myself against, but with many houses close by, stretching in both directions, that I longed to escape out of the front door to explore. Soon to discover, this was not permitted. Short walks on a tight lead, were the regime with my new family. And I adapted...not so voluntarily however...
Mamma C, (this was the mother of the two lovely creatures for whom I had been transported away from my farm and family), I sensed immediate affection from, but she spent far too much time with the 2 house cats, Tabbi, a long haired and rather whiffy but, overall, quite sociable mog, and James, an oversized jet black, and far more challenging and disagreeable animal altogether.
These poor felines had travelled back from Italy- a land far, far away, and a constantly mentioned subject, with Mamma C, and my angels. They had arrived only recently, in this country, and were still acclimatising themselves to being in

new surroundings, and to, la Grandmere, the doubting older lady, and owner of the house, we were now living in.
"La Nanny", who, had her own "house" dog, Giulia - a sweet tempered, but somewhat confused shih-tsu, who was, it had to be said the most welcoming of them all, and with her own history, years in the Czech Republic, ok- but who knew where that was? She, I could barely understand, but appreciated her immediate and uncomplicated comradery, albeit, she had free run of this enormous house, up the stairs, and down, up the lushly carpeted stairs, where my angels disappeared to sleep, at a certain hour, While I was pushed into a gated cage, with many kisses and much persuasive conviction, at night. Down in the deep darkness of the kitchen.
Just a short time, I had with my angels, for whom I had been bought, as a sort of male substitute for a father, this I overheard, but never really understood. He no longer lived with the family.
Sophia, the elder of the 2, rather feisty, hesitant at times, when not incredibly and demonstrably affectionate, and Isabella, the younger, who had held me for years in her dreams, who dedicated herself most completely to my training, which I have to confess I enjoyed - enticed by streams of doggy treats.

I learned quickly to sit, lie down, beg for the queen, pray, with my paws stretching upwards, roll over, and run through inflatable tunnels, then fetch- the last , being my only bid for independence, when I would frequently obediently run after the ball or stick, and then race off with huge satisfaction, ignoring the pleading calls to 'heel' and disappear in the undergrowth of the garden to a safe place where I could peacefully shred it to small pieces: I was a terrier after all, and very much male, and my place in the house must be firmly and unequivocally established.

From the confines of my cage down in the kitchen, which I did not initially disagree with, all kinds of delicious meals and treats prepared there. Bowls of varying sizes, which, when both cats in their continued sufferance or Giulia, in defiance of a change of diet, would leave for me to surreptitiously gobble down, unseen by “la Grandmere” or Mamma C- all seemed most satisfactory, as an alternative to my past frugal existence on the farm.

Then, one fine day, came the cases, plastic wheely containers that I could easily have fitted in, and often did, hiding beneath the freshly laundered shirts and trousers, thinking it a new magnificent game, I could roll around, bite and shake. Cross expressions and angry words, and then, indelibly, they closed the zips, tightly fastened.

Mamma C and the girls with a vague sense of apprehension and excitement left, out of the front door, early evening, as the misty, wavering English sun gave way to early evening, they went.

Backward glances, initially full of regret, and then, complete absence....and Loss, an empty chasm that dragged my belly low to the ground.

I attempted to follow- these were my people now, I belonged with them. “No Max” (for this was my new name) “you stay”. Locked in my cage, I was bereft and confused. Why had I been left behind? As night fell, and the dark clouds settled over the house, I missed with an indistinguishable pain, my girls and howled in my misery.

Grandmere did not appreciate my continued miserable behaviour, for which my only solace, a newfound rubbing myself on any surface, which brought a simple and fleeting pleasure, but in some way, helped to pass the time- and Giulia, had taken on a newfound attraction for me, which only seemed to anger the old lady more. She delivered swift and painful kicks as I mounted her docile and ever more confused, but highly attractive powder puff of a dog.

There followed a rather painful and drug induced stay at the vets, my mating life had been brutally foreshortened. There would be no more of that revolting sexy rubbing against

furniture and more importantly, absolutely no mounting of Giulia, for me!
I was returned by a friendly and smiling green vested vet to the house. Dazed and a bit sore, between my hindlegs, with a huge Elizabethan ruff on my neck, I slept, peacefully, mostly in my cage. Much frustration and the most enormous fatigue, I could not even muster the energy to lick my wounds. Intervals on a tight lead to do my duty in the luscious garden, that I longed to race around and discover eventual escape routes to the huge sheltering trees in the gardens beyond. I wondered if this was to be my new life.
I watched as la grandmere, in her candlewick dressing gown, shuffled her way around from the kitchen to the chesterfield from feeding duties to the television, grumbling her complaints at my tuneful howling of the previous nights... I gazed hopefully up at her anyway, my tummy always overdue for breakfast, always.
Giulia came to greet me, amiably, with stiff and smelly whiskers, at my cage door, as it was cautiously opened. It was late summer, and a coolish breeze greeted my welcoming nostrils, I padded towards the back door, Grandmere gently released me, finally from my collar. Giulia in tow, I completed a tour of inspection of the garden, marking a few

of the terracotta pots, weekly, my legs still pathetically feeble.

The inconfundible smell of fox still lingered in the camellias, though not fresh ... it must be covered... and a wild rabbit had been spotted making itself at home by the stone statue of the lovers- this was not to be tolerated! I must have fallen into a light doze on the soft spongy moss in the dappled shade of the copper beech tree: mesmerised, as watching the breeze ripple through the leaves twisting and tossing them in its wake.

A small burst of cross wind chased through the house... and I sensed a fragrance I definitely recognised... that hint of vanilla mixed with soft female teenage perspiration. I sat up alert, my paws warm in the sun. Barely breathing for the ecstatic waves of pure joy that rolled over and enveloped me...I barked ... and barked.... Yes! It was them! They had come back to get me!

I ran at top speed, all frailty forgotten, literally, as fast as my short but perfectly formed legs would carry me, practically flying. it seemed, around, over the long chairs, in the garden, rebounding into the soft cushions of the sofas in the sitting room, through the opened back door, and relaunching into the garden, slaloming though the terracotta pots, all the while yipping, yapping and squealing at the top of my puppy range... barking and barking... I could hear in the very back of my consciousness, voices reprimanding “No... No... NO!” ... but my joy was too great, they were back, and what other way did I have of showing them?

Isabella, the legginess of a young foal, covered me in soft kisses as she giggled under my rain of excited licks, Sophia, all warmth, and athletic cuddles, smilingly but gently grasped my head and ruffled my ears, then the mother, Mamma C.

Laughing eyes, and that deep voice I sensed , that could change mood in a fraction of a second, from gentle canoodling and wheedling to a fierce bark of command, and I correctly understood that it would be important for me to follow her changing thoughts, as it would be she , smelling distantly of wild figs and vanilla, who would in the days, weeks, months and years to follow, who would serve as doctor in prescribing change of diet when my tum was a bit loose,, put drops in my ears and eyes with passing infections, stick thermometers indelicately up my bottom, which would habitually be rewarded with a ferocious nip, that she deftly and almost always successfully escaped, cook and serve me farm chicken thighs braised in olive oil, and take me on daily walks, come rain, snow or shine, through the fields of sheep , cows and horses.

Months of family life tumbled comfortably into one another, as we moved home, town and county, to Tenterden, in nearby Kent. The girls started their new schools in this new life in England.

They would leave early in the morning, in sombre black uniforms, with moods to match, as I returned from my 6 am walk across the rec and into the fields behind the leisure centre, with my new found band of doggy friends: Timmy, a retired greyhound, who lived above the electrical shop opposite, and for such an elegant, beautifully honed muscular canine example of perfection, produced the stinkiest and surprisingly numerous piles of poo, executed most inelegantly: Pippin, a loving and clumsy retriever, Tallulah, a somewhat irritable Norfolk terrier, Nelson, my favourite friend, and rather handsome Irish terrier, whose owner however was not so keen, as I had, on occasion, when on long Sunday walks in the fields behind St. Mildred's, led him through dense thickets of thorny brambles, and then emerged miles further along the track , having lost him with his head stuck down a rabbit or badger hole: and Bella, a small and skinny dog, white with oddly placed brown patches-sort of gave the impression of generations of deprivation, but she was my running and chasing partner, and we would spend hours on the Rec, as winter subsided, and the days got longer and warmer.

Chapter Two: An unexpected partenza

Watery sunlight seeps through the shadows of the over-hanging trees in our damp and unkempt garden- on racing out, I just caught sight of a tail, an extremely fluffy ginger and white one- that damned next door neighbour cat was taking it all too far, and how could it be so fast at 5 in the morning?

There had been a strange sense of excitement and anticipation in the days preceding, much animated chattering, and the bedroom doors upstairs kept tightly and mysteriously shut. Tabitha and James, the house cats, had been curiously transported off in the back of the new (old second hand) mini, that Mamma C, had surreptitiously" done a deal" in the Waitrose car park, to a dodgy, dark faced, father and son from Faversham, relinquishing the old faithful and Italian plated Peugeot.

Mamma C and Sophia, left ,with cats and copious supplies of lily’s kitchen pouches and kibble... and it had to be said, I sort of missed my daily adventures with them... Tabbi , I had learned to accept a sort of resentful cohabitation with, she was old ,rather short sighted, noisy and affectionate, and as long as she steered clear of my kibble dish,

which, I had had to educate her by pinning her against the wainscoting one morning catching the little minx , daring to help herself, was now far more respectful and kept her distance. It can be said, we jogged along fairly peaceably.
James, on the other hand, had established an immediate enmity on meeting on the landing stairs, some months ago, when she had drawn herself up most imposingly, hissing wildly, had painfully scratched my unsuspecting morositas nose with a sharply hewn claw and drawn blood.
I took every opportunity, after that episode, to chase her down the garden, and attempt to rip that long black thrashing tail from its hub... One day...
Kibble? Now why kibble? I absolutely never had biscuits for breakfast and was suitably outraged. should I show my contempt by ignoring them and wait? I sensed not... Banging and scraping noises on the stairs assaulted my ears, an assortment of overcrammed cases and bags spilling out with bikini bras, and beach towels were being dragged down, by Mamma C and Isabella out to the road in front of the house, Sophia had the duty of staying with me to ensure I ate something. “Sbrigati Max” she cajoled, I snaffled down the contents of the dish- sensing the futility in waiting for something better to be presented, and my bone shaped tray and

dishes were instantly snatched up, washed and put in another of those capacious plastic bags.

No walk this morning then, I ingeniously ascertained. My lead clipped on, I was smartly trotted out to the road, following on from the succession of baggages, already stowed on top of the mini, in the top box, and up to the roof in the double doored boot, others crushed to one side in the back of the car, where I would sit with my young angel.

Roughly shoved by Isabella, less angelic and more impatient this morn, with encouraging noises, in the slightly ridiculous and ineffectual side door, I took my refuge under the seat, and attempted to calm a rising sense of anxiety.

As you now know, I greatly disliked travelling in the car, and the loud roar of traffic unnerved me, but the thing I hated most of all, was being left by my family, and so the decision had been made to take me with them.

In preparation I had been bathed the evening before by Isabella, “He stinks” she had shrieked excitedly, smothering me in stifling perfumed bath essence, Sophia had dried me in one of those crispy rough towels, reserved for my usage, " Don’t give me those sideways eyes" she had giggled, but I knew secretly, that it still unnerved her when I did so.

The air had that fresh dampness that very early mornings in July in the southeast, often bring- a sharp almost fruity

smell of ripening flowers and perhaps the scent brought by the surrounding vineyards and orchards, as we wound our way through the villages, and across the Romney marshes in the pale golden hue of the rising mist down towards Folkestone. Very few cars at all, and a sense of happy expectancy filled our mini, as we drew into the harbour area.
We dragged slowly through several checkpoints, and to a large car park, where we docked and, I was led to sort of a faux grassed enclosure to perform my morning ablutions, along with many other apprehensive and inquisitive mutts... I was initially a bit doubting of this strange bouncy astroturf, with malingering odours of poo poos long past, albeit the shiny green appearance.
The "field" was surrounded by a selection of metallic poo bag distributors and bins. A particularly lively little schnauzer caught my eye, and we were off in a chase- that and the sharp salty sea air, I had no problem at all with my performance.
The girls had headed off to a large low glassy mirrored building, on the opposite side of the road, and had returned with warm and fragrant pastries and rich smelling coffee.
Having breakfasted, (Sophia kindly tore me off a large piece of her “Pain au raisin”) we now drove off to another of the

buildings- orange in colour and with PETS hugely indicating its otherwise empty facade.

The mini parked up outside, Mamma C accompanied me to yet another checkpoint, where 2 smiling and pleasant ladies, also dressed in orange, checked my pet passport and that all vaccinations were in order.

I was subsequently heaved up onto a slippery desk, never one to make it easy, I whined painfully. abhorring the merest hint of any physical "control" check. One of them, checked my eyes and ears and had a quick feel of my tummy area- I growled as she lifted my tail, at which she decided hastily, and wisely, not to take my temperature.

Back to the mini again, and onto yet another sort of booth, a grey one this time, a shard of sunlight caught my eyes and made me wince. A bespectacled flabby grey uniformed man, standing behind a glass partition in the hut, peered down into our car. " Hmmm 3 passengers, 1 dog..." All good, papers and documents passed back to Mamma C, and off we drove... to another queue... Good Lord! It all seemed interminable, this fretful waiting for acceptance to continue the next part of or journey... This time a blue hut, and a little man in smart dark navy uniform with an impressively clipped moustache- who amicably waved us on -no document checks here, and back out into the light ...... to join another line of cars, behind an enormous red traffic light.

The girls got out of the car to take some photographs with their iPhones in this golden light of the new morning. I was far too exhausted by the mystery that awaited, and so remained curled tightly around myself, eyes firmly shut, thoughts of Bella and our morning chases, passed through my anguished mind.

I sensed as we started moving very slowly again, and 2 young women, in official looking orange jackets directed us onto the very narrow entrance to the train in waiting, down below.

I caught a last whiff of iodine-soaked air as we entered the darkened carriage in a line of cars. Cars in front, cars behind, a whole train loaded with... cars. The huge barriers whooshed closed as a suppressed clanging of a bell rang out, and the train moved smoothly, and almost silently, out of Folkestone dock.

Paralysed with fear, I sensed movement of which I could not understand, and so remained, rigidly, in my position of safety, despite Isabella's attempts to tease me out of my lair. All was a murky darkness- a shadowy grey gloom, occasionally broken by a fragmented amber light winking bleakly at the end of the long narrow car lounge. It was the strangest and most unpleasant sensation, of pushing at speed, through a tiny aperture with the threatening weightlessness of millions of fishy tons of brine all around me.

I felt both dizzy and sick, and mildly in shock, wishing Isabella had not gone into such detail, in kindly explaining this part of the journey to me. I could see Sophia felt the same, motionless and wide eyed. The other 2 unaffected, seemingly, chatted about this and that. I reorganised my paws carefully, giving them a dry tongued lick and tried to settle, praying for this to be over.

With the hugest relief imaginable, DJ Khaled and Rhianna blaring out from the radio were the first sign... and with that a tiny pale greyish spot of light up ahead, rapidly growing in size, until the whole carriage was illuminated with a warm rosy light of early morning.

At Last! I blinked my eyes through my heavy gingery lashes, we had surfaced from that devilish mole hole, of a tunnel.

Driving meekly off the train, as if playing a game of follow my leader, onto a wide road with a huge board signposting!

PARIS, DIEPPE, LUXEMBOURG, ROUENS, RHEIMS, NANCY, STRASBOURG, LYON.

Mamma C kept her silence, I really hoped she knew where we were heading. Sombrely and slowly following the cars in front of us, we drove through a high fenced area topped with barbed wire. The road bottlenecked and we were forced into another queue, inching forward at walking pace, the windows open, I could sense the stench of acrid human sweat on the air mixed with a seriously unpleasant rotten fishy and vegetable odour, entering the AC from outside.
A barren, treeless wasteland. What was this place? Groups of dark figures stared aggressively from behind the fencing at us, clinging to it with their bony fingers, and I heard the girls mumbling about “the Jungle".
It smelled fetid, and of human desperation. I felt relieved to be moving through and away from this place so full of sadness, hatred, and impending explosive tension...
Several animated discussions, waving around of maps and spurious pages of printed directions with colourful lines running down them, that had been so carefully printed and planned in the weeks preceding the journey were now flapping back and forth, but the only decision, they seemed to agree on was NOT to take the direction for Paris.

Apparently Zio David (Mamma C's brother), and a regular traveller in France, had warned us to avoid at all costs, taking the very tantalising, and repetitious signs for PARIS... having once landed up , trapped, in his very English car, in the multi lane , total confusion around the Arc de Triomphe, where all but him, knew exactly where they were going, and very impatiently, made him realise the foreign idiot he was.

Thereby, with an encouraging burst of speed, we took the autoroute signposted for Nancy, (among a myriad of other places), and hoped against hope we would not have to back track... There was a great sense of excitement at being just in France, away from England, and on our way to ... well in fact, I had absolutely no idea. But the air smelled differently, the light gentler and more golden, and I shared the family's' sense of adventure.

The urgency to complete as much of the trip, as quickly as possible, forced Mamma C's foot down heavily on the accelerator pedal, and we tore away at great speed, laughingly overtaking a seemingly endless stream of French, German, and Dutch trucks, all going in our direction, to the south, on the inside lane.

Such was the lively conversation and plans for the days ahead, thoughts in airy dreams of sun-baked beaches and

delicious feasts al fresco, in the olive grove; that none of them had noticed a rather small, and not so repetitive sign-post indicating “Travaux”.
The car floor was hutting up under my belly, despite the fleecy towel as my cooling barrier, and I kneaded my paws to rearrange it, unhappily, searching for comfort, sensing something imminent... but what?
From our breakneck speed (“Let’s see how fast the car can actually go”, dares light-heartedly thrown out...)
Free from the boring constrictions of the English motor-ways, Mamma C let rip, and we were shooting down the overtaking lane at around 110 mph, when, unanticipatedly, she slammed on the brakes and came to a squealing halt, as the lane we were flying down without a care, was blocked inexplicably, by a series of large heavy plastic orange barriers and cones.
Dismay, and a heavy grey smoke filled the car, as the line of trucks, we had gaily left for dust, just minutes before, now chundered noisily and determinedly past us, on the inside lane, along with the hundreds of wiser and more cautious motorists who had attentively observed the road sign-posts.
Some of the Camion drivers hooted deafeningly on their klaxons, both amused, and in warning? Really? of the

impending danger, noticing Mamma C attempting to edge sneakily into their lane. They were unable to stop, with their heavy loads. We were forced to come to a complete halt, in dire humiliation .... and wait, impatiently for the tiniest gap in the surging traffic, to leap into the inside lane, and accelerate terrifyingly, whizzing up through the gears achieving the obligatory 90 kph and stay in line, in a far more docile attitude, for the next 20 km of the French autoroute.

I popped my head up to scrutinise my surroundings from the car window, providing a welcome moment of attention focused on my comfort, hitherto ignored, in the mounting excitement of speed. Isabella reorganised my bedding sweetly.

Miles and miles of tightly grown greenish gold fields of corn and barley- a fresh tangy smell, new to my nostrils- and nothing else... no cows, or pigs, grazing in habitual ignorance of the streams of smelly cars and trucks passing in their midst

Lack of sleep and of interest in the poor visual variety forced me back down to my less heated and more comfortable nest under the seat.

A few hours later, we sashayed moderately up to one of the superbly equipped “Aree de services”. Excellent, I needed a drink, and also, a wee. I bounded off, released from the confines of the car, into a closely wooded area and let rip - my eyes, half closed in a near ecstatic moment.... heavenly relief! what a strange odour - pungent and fruity, and a rather revolting, yet familiar, animal stink of fear. Undoubtedly explained by a sparsely bearded man, who had urgently pulled up in an old rusty van, pulling a trailer, noses dry with fright, dozens of trembling sheep, gasped in the warm air through the tiny slats.

I took a few hasty laps of water, and wandered cautiously and a bit stunned, back to my retreat, in the relative safety of the mini. In this case I had no curiosity to investigate further. Mamma C and the girls took turns in the metallic domed cylinder labelled "Toilette", and we returned back on the autoroute again.

The sun beat strongly on the windscreen, and the AC struggled to keep our interior minimally, well not exactly cool, but at a warmish temperature, even my cool towel had warmed up uncomfortably, to an over cosy heat. Conversation had dropped to a peaceful lull, and wistful complaints about the repetition of the musical tracks that Skyrock radio played, when there was a loud bang, followed by a threatening, popping sound from the front of the car, the engine under the bonnet.

I cocked my ear in anticipation of something awful about to happen...
Mamma C's face had turned to a strange pallor under her already bronzed face- and the girls chattered nervously like frightened monkeys. We lurched jerkily into the next "area de service" and, at a very low speed indeed. Isabella and I took advantage to relieve ourselves, as much from nerves as actual need.
Mamma C, helped by Sophia perused the dials and levels on the dashboard, and flicked through the pages of the mini clubman manual, desperately searching for a solution, or indeed, any kind of explanation for the improvised "malessere" of our vehicle.
A rather strong metallic and acrid smell was issuing from the bonnet of the car, and it was decided, probably better NOT to try and open it- as they would have had no idea what to do in any case.
So, fingers crossed, and kisses on fingers to all and any of the saints who were observing our journey from above, we set off again, hotter and sweatier than before, with the added tension of "would the car actually make the journey?"
We had been on the road for about 9 hours now, and above all, Mamma C was really very tired, as were we all! so it

was decided to try and make it to Lyon, where Mamma C had booked a hotel for the night.
No idea of what had burst or busted in the engine, and of course, not being covered by the AA or Rac, green card etc. being a family who lived by our pants, constantly risking, just making ends meet on a monthly basis, rarely opportunities for any extras or luxuries, like travel insurance- these were not expenses that could be afforded in our travel plans!
We limped carefully along, the car incapable of accelerating. It felt as though a humongously large mass pressed down on the engine, phials of charcoal smoke wheedling out, if any speed was attempted.
We travelled in a rigidly tense, heart beating silence... as if waiting for the car itself to make the next move. The Lyon exit, could not have come soon enough, and we attempted some crumb of relief, slowly following the "Toutes les directions" signs, round and round the city's peripheries, straining our eyes tightly, in the hope of finding some indication of our elusive" Ibis" hotel, when at a certain point, the family's mobile phones, for which they seemed to depend for navigation and information , shut down, with a complete lack of signal.
All hope of finding the hotel in this huge sprawling city was abandoned. A mounting impatience, and growing sense of

desperation to find a place to stop and rest... at least for a few hours, was palpable.

We had been around the city centre, agilely avoiding the steep tramline ridges, dividing up the lanes of traffic and sending us off to "le centre commercial", and back, several times.

The hotel chosen, had been such, for its close proximity to the autoroute exit,, but 3 hours of navigating around Lyon, with zero assistance, had taken Mamma C to snapping point of fatigue, and sensing the potentially dynamite tension in the car, I curled myself into an even tinier ball on the floor of the car, and imagined myself, not there at all, but chasing through the kingcups, in my favourite meadow behind St Mildreds', wind in my ears , and fresh dewy grass under my bounding paws.

Having decided that 12 hours on the road was ENOUGH! and, given the poor reduced state of the mini clubman, who however slowly robustly soldiered on, in its abjectly and most evident injured condition.

We, reluctantly, but resignedly, turned into a Camion Park" on the side of the autoroute, just past Lyon. Trucks, astoundingly as far as the eyes could see in this enormous stretch of roadside resting point, we came to a stop,

ridiculously diminutive, between 2 towering metallic beasts of camions.
Heaving back the long front seats as far as the lumpen luggage inside would allow, the girls attempted to make of the car, as acceptable a sleeping area as possible Mamma C. suggested she sleep in the overhead coffin of a top box, such was her exhaustion, and absolute need to be out of the constricting driving seat.
Sophia headed off to the rather rustic "lavabo", provided for the truck drivers overnight stays, and on her return, the family collapsed into a fitful version of rest, uncaring and probably also, unaware of the inappropriately masculine setting of their surroundings.
I attempted to sleep on this starlit night, resting on Mamma C's legs, but was startled into alarm each time, one of the enormous trucks, cab lights glaring, rumbled discreetly, out of the park, to continue on its journey.
At the approaching dawn, a vague misty pinkish hue replaced the deep indigo curtain of the night.
I had resolutely stretched myself across the scrunched-up bodies of the girls in the back, who, loudly complaining, rudely shifted me off, commenting on my redolent cheesiness.

The heat had reached an unbearable point with 3 human bodies and one dog. Far too much for a small mini clubman interior to sustain... And so, we also, moved cautiously away from our dock, the car, showing no indication at that moment of any immediate problems. The 5-hour repose had possibly done some good.

We sleepily entered the first area of services, the bar not yet open, Mamma C and the girls went inside the pale pink tiled "salle de bains" if you could call it that, in no way ideal, but it gave them space to wash and quickly change.

The girls, as Mamma C's daughters, had learned to become quite the stoics in these situations, and accepted the basic but clean (at least at this time of the morning) with relatively few comments or complaints.

The bar, which had now opened, could not have seemed more welcoming, Mamma C took a cafe' creme, and the girls chocolat chauds with voluptuously warm croissants, and brioches., to alert the senses.

Mamma C seemed almost back on form again, despite the very minimal 3 hours of actual sleep.

The thought of setting out on the autoroute again, was as unthinkably unbearable to me, as it was to my little Isabella, who whined and whimpered, overtired, miserable, at not being able to stretch out properly, ached all over.

Already sweaty, I commiserated entirely. We both longed for a comfortable bed. Maybe tonight?
The mini, having completely reawaken, now set to heaving audibly, despite its replenishing of oil and petrol Mamma C had hoped it would "buck up", but it faltered its way ahead, undoubtedly not helped by its extremely heavy load.
It was decided, far too risky to entertain the AC being switched on, so we pootered along in the "camions lents" lane, absolutely spent of any energy to consider overtaking even the slowest of vans, driven, by fag smoking evil looking old grandmeres.
The girls were humiliated at our crazily slow progress, a long way from our courageous and spavaldo start of journey. The excited and emotive squeals of "Let's see how fast it can go?!!" ... a distant and rather bitter memory.
We started on a series of terrifyingly narrow, to my mind, tunnels... one after another... we were at the Frejus pass...
I felt very fortunate, strangely to be flattened on the bottom of the car, under my seat.
No sooner had we gratefully come out of one, to be blasted with the dazzling morning sunlight ... than we entered another, dimly lit, chamber of exhaust fumes... dangerously close to our friends, the camionisti, charging down on us,

on the other side of the road, but at what seemed literally only centimetres of distance.

One flashed its headlights and nearly blasted us out of our senses with its horn, as Mamma C had started veering ever so slightly into the centre of the road. She was evidently suffering the effects of precious little sleep and the temporary caffeine shot of the cafe creme, was already wearing off.

She seemed almost drugged and was driving perilously close to the middle of the road, both the motorists behind us, and the oncoming camionisti, bearing down on us, headlights blaring, horns honking wildly. We were avoiding them with the merest whisker of a chance.

I popped my head up only once and shot straight down again in an attempt to recompose myself, my eyes rigidly shutting out this continuing cacophonous nightmare.

Would we ever make it?? WHERE WERE WE GOING??? AND WHY?

Sometimes a poor dogs' lot can just be a bit too much to bear, so I sulked silently on my overheated fleecy towel, that had not been aired or refreshed, of course , to afford me even the most meagre of comforts under my seat, occasionally bearing my teeth at Isabella, as she gently made to scratch my back on that especially sensitive bit, where I had

had a most aggressive flea attack some time ago, and the skin was till sensitive as hell.

The memory still sharp, I had never been so close to chewing my own tail off in anger and desperation. I drifted off in an agitated paw jerking miserable attempt at sleep, which seemed unsuccessful.

Then, quite abruptly, tempted by the meaty whiff of a treat, I awoke refreshed!

Chapter Three: BENVENUTO IN ITALIA

I raised my muzzle, heavy but high in expectation. Finally, I would discover, at last, this land, that that my family recounted so many stories of, often dewy eyed and always melancholy.

The enthusiasm, passion, the loves and lasting friendships, the laughter and spontaneity. The complete madness at times... where my girls had been born and grown up.

Where Mamma C, in her very early twenties had left behind her London life, in a wonderful exchange for "Il Bel Paese".

The music changed instantly, as did the mood, the mini was filled with the deep melodic voice of Tiziano Ferro- away from the black and repetitive drill and jungle tracks of France -- so much stronger, masculine, yet full of life- was this the sound that was Italian music? IT WAS, at least for my family.

His soundtracks had followed them from birth to their formation and personal choices- often a companion signifying important moments and memories. The radio always on in the bathroom, or in the car going to school, or visiting places, at weekends, they sang along remembered choruses, giggled and sighed over moments long past.

Being a strictly Anglo-Saxon dog myself, of impeccable lineage. I rather wondered, in my cool but attentive audience, at the fuss they made.

Encouraged by the congenial and relaxed atmosphere, created by my travelling companions, I felt courageous enough to inspect. And ventured up onto the tight space between the bundled bags and Isabella.

Ahead of us, white peaked mountainous masses- new to me- the air so sharply fresh, so clear, windows wound down completely- they wanted to breathe again, the smell of home.

Our first stop, in an “area di servizio” at Aosta, my first little passeggiata, and absolutely necessary marking of territory, the grass much crisper and greener.

The girls entered into a glass panelled shop, and some minutes later, came out, smilingly loaded with local cheeses, and Mamma C, with grappa and bottles of wine as gifts - more weight for the poor mini!

I was, however, quite astonished at how the mini seemed to have, at last, partially recovered. After the regular and short stops, it seemed to, if only momentarily, have taken courage to get some sort of speed up.

Could it be perhaps, that we were on a gradual downhill run? For an hour or so, it accelerated off, in an almost lively spate. Mamma C still drove somewhat cautiously, dreading the worst.

On our heading into Genova, predictably, it returned to its flagging and snail like pace, nothing above a stately 50/60 kph. Sparkling silver and metallic, black gleaming cars shot past us like catapults, eager to get to wherever they were going.

No speed limits here apparently. The autostradas, wide but quite dull. I fell into another peremptory and uncomfortable doze, following some most peculiar chicken, from a road-side sandwich that Isabella was battling her way through, and had fed me unlikely looking niblets, I suspected of what looked like cockcomb and quite possibly ghizzard or there-abouts, quite indigestible for my tastes.

They had completely different traditions for how to enjoy chicken here, known as "Il cibreo" in Florentine dialect, it was considered a treat in mostly Tuscany, so Sophia reliably informed me.

She loved all of these Tuscan specialities, and excitedly described to me, such delizie as Trippa alla fiorentina, panino al lampredotto o poppa, crusty panini served from steaming little trailers, loaded with boiled cows intestines or udders, and accompanied by a very bright green parsley sauce.

I, like Isabella, suspected I would be less keen and drooped into another snooze, my snout twitching, dreaming of the traditional Sunday roast, and the pickings Mamma C, tossed to Giulia and I, following the weekly lunch at Nanny's home, back in Blighty.

Awoken by a sensation of anguish and a wave of intense heat in the car, I lifted my head and popped onto the seat, uncomfortably, next to Isabella. What was this?

My paws felt unstable, and I retched sickeningly, from side to side. We were passing through the middle of yellow and terracotta stuccoed buildings, washing lines with greying vests and pants flapping improbably in the gusty breeze, hung from wrought iron terraces.

We were on an ostensibly thin strip of road, precariously suspended by huge swaying struts attached far up on giant metal girders. It appeared to have been hewn neatly in the midst of the city. I felt distinctly sick...

The Morandi bridge. I could just catch sight of the clear blue of the Mediterranean, glittering temptingly in the distance, a tiny and fast disappearing v of sea, in this tumbling mess of buildings massed together.

A faint scent of salty iodine, that my nostrils caught surreptitiously, momentarily calmed the rising wave of vomit rising from my belly and piqued the smoky exhaust fumes that filled the car.

The traffic here was intense, so many cars, so many HGVs, I was sure I could feel the bridge below the car wheels, vaguely rocking from side to side. Unnerved by this new sensation, I returned down under the seat, this time to the safety of my basket and its tartan cushion, fleecy towel scratched impatiently aside, which felt distinctly safer.

Following an excited and very angry exchange of opinions between Mamma C and Sophia regarding the exact position of the turn off for Firenze and Tuscany; the sign posting along this bridge was at best, approximate.

Mamma C effected a chaotic and noisy, with much blaring of car and truck horns, maneuver, cutting swiftly into the outside lane, and swerving dangerously in front of a surging lane of very fast-moving cars, and we shot off, ignoring the insults, with only a couple of fingered gesticulations, out of the car window, onto the tangenziale turn off, leading down towards Tuscany.

Another series of those dark and deathly tunnels, however, better spaced and with slightly fewer cars, and far less trucks and we were decisively, down on the gentle descent from Genova in the heart of Liguria-on the coastal part of the autostrada.

Enchanting pointy hills, all fascinatingly terraced with ancient olive trees and arrays of beautiful pink and red flowers. Oleanders, thrust their fulsome blooms through the gated divides of the autostrada, promising a wonderful perspective of Italian summertime.

A sense of calm and happiness pervaded the atmosphere in the mini.

Finally! I sensed in some way we had passed the worst parts of our journey. The shimmering azure of the sea to our left, we passed down through Rapallo and Imperia. Even the names conjured a glamorous sensation of impressive places.

Windows slid right down, the air that filled the car was full of warm expectancy and excitement, that made me feel, suddenly extremely tired, and so, I settled back on to my comforting tartan cushion to fall into another of my more relaxed reposes.

A sharp shock of cypress scent reawakened me. The staggering view of these mighty shapes that almost blocked the light, at intervals, and softly swaying umbrella pines mixed with salty sand, and we had passed from Liguria, into the girl's beloved homeland of Toscana.

Toscana, that I had heard so much about. The land of their birth and growing up, where they had made their first friends, fought their first fights, through the elementare school, surrounded by family and friends- the names I had heard so frequently repeated, Pietro, Viola, Alma, Federico... Sara, Egle, Virginia and Rebecca, all the childhood friends my girls had left behind, for their new life in England.

I was apprehensive but sensing their innate happiness, very curious to meet all, or at least some of these Italian humans.

I stretched my paws and yawned loudly.

The heat of the afternoon sun settled on the roof of the little car. We cracked on courageously, Mamma C at a point beyond exhaustion , was running on pure adrenalin, with the anticipation and joy of arrival in touching distance, the girls, both of them sentient of the situation, kept the windows wide open, knowing, she would keep her energy going, for the imminent return, and I, given our slow pace , took advantage, and shoved my overheated head out of the back window, feeling the warm Tuscan breezes splay the feathered fronds of my ears.

Mamma C was feeling and flavouring the familiarity of her past life. Passing by Capannori, Lucca, Pontedera.... the sun, a deep pulsing orange, the warm early evening gusts passing through the car windows. She was calm and happy to be back.

The peace in our tiny space, despite a fleet of carefree travellers returning from a day out at the Tuscan beaches, less frenetic, and more flexibly, following a day on the beach. Sunburned, more respectful of the speed traps, on the familiar old FIPILI, the superstrada, that the family had travelled so many times, on Sophia's many away games for volleyball.

So many memories that they discussed laughingly, remembering both absurd and familiar characters. Team companions, over precious mothers and competitive fathers on the sidelines. Every weekend, they had raced in the tiny first navy-blue Peugeot, up and down to various fixtures, almost always late, my poor Sophia!

Chapter Four: L’arrivo a Montespertoli

Ginestra Fiorentina. This was our exit! The light waning, the sun was an ebbing ball of red molten lava on the horizon. A fluorescent blue cross up in the hills, at San Michele, announced our arrival, brightening in the encompassing dusk. Up to the Tuscan hills, 10 minutes before Florence itself, the softly undulating and verdant hills, stippled with flashes of the brightest saffron yellow of gorse flowers- and a smell, fresh and sweet, yet almost surgically clean- as the light slowly foundered- we wound our way up the narrowest of lanes. Thankfully Mamma C knew these routes so well. The way homes. A true zig zag of a road, up to the mount. The girls recounted a memory of some years ago. Their father’s car had been stuck halfway up the hill, blocked in a blizzard, when, hand brake locked on, he had left the car, hopeful that with all of the cars blocked behind, they would find it again the next day. The faltering mini, on its last legs most literally, grasped its way up the last hill, hairpin bend by hairpin bend' painfully struggling over... The thought of being on the point of toppling over, one of the ever-tightening roads, and rolling over and over to the bottom of the valley, ran briefly through my mind, but was quickly dispelled, as we laboriously made it to the top.

Mamma C's face, a picture of strained torment. A cluster of rather ugly 1970s apartment blocks in lurid yellows and grey streaked dirty whites to the left, while to the right a long-abandoned stone-built farmhouse from the Napoleonic era, savagely gated and chained, with many a heavy padlock, "INGRESSO PROIBITO" on a half hanging off metal sign with rusted bullet holes through it, crumbled gently away, in a scrubby wasteland of softly swaying grasses. How I would have loved, right now, to chase through those grasses, snapping them in my jaws, the warm pungent scented earth under my paws, to scratch and roll around and to stretch my paws out fully in the late afternoon sun. Not long now, I could hear the anticipation in their voices that we were imminently to arrive... through a wide avenue of tall and fragrant cypresses, the last of the bleeding red sun flashed in my eyes at uncomfortable intervals, making me feel a bit dizzy, then the slow ascent of what looked a perfectly innocent soft green hill... what were they doing behind it? Two dump trucks lurched suspiciously and noisily around the corner towards us... suddenly our noses were assaulted with the most disgusting stink, "Eurghhhhhh!!!" the girls physically recoiled and slamming their hands and clumsy fingers on the buttons to hastily shut the car windows, attempted to cover their faces. The deplorable stench was IN the car at that point, the vilest concoction of rotting fish and meat, combined with diarrhoea, vomit and an acidic chemical undertone. Two words, "LA DISCARICA". In this charmingly unblemished corner of Tuscany, the local authorities had decided wisely, and possibly with some huge financial gain in view, to place one of the largest municipal dumps or tips. MEMO: Next time, they would make sure the windows were as hermetically sealed as possible, well before arriving anywhere near it. Their discomfort amused me in my ridiculously fatigued state, the stench was indeed unpleasant, but speaking personally, not so bad. "Bar Silvano" lay to our left, and an ancient old man, covered with warts or moles, his back bent, wearing a sweaty looking singlet and grey baggy shorts, half grizzled a smile, showing a few brown teeth, as we passed by. Then, a clearing with a church, whitewashed facade, and stippled painted doors that were tightly closed against the sun. A slim, black haired and bearded man, with large heavily lidded eyes, appeared before us on the dust path, this was Stefano, he had come up some steps from a group of rustic looking dwellings facing the church, "Ciao Tutte!" he greeted us, "E questo? chi è?" he bent over to inspect me more closely, his breath was thick with coffee and stale cigar, and his body smelt ripe with a bloom of the day's sweat- but who was I to complain? At my cheesiest ever, probably, the anguish and terrors of the trip redolent in my tufted fur. Stefano Hugged Mamma C, who practically collapsed into his embrace, and each of the girls affectionately. I liked this man immediately. and licked his hand enthusiastically to show it: then a woman, far too thin and bony. with a nervous energy that spooked me, Maria, dressed in white, came running towards us, "MAAAAAAX!" she yelled in her shrill and raucous voice, she had a vaguely unclean smell, unwashed, and a head of thick bushy hair, her face as bony and brittle as her body, she grabbed hold of me and kissed me, lifting me by my front paws, and smothering me in her skeletal frame... behind her I could spot, closely following, a patched ginger, white and black cat, arching its back at me and hissing with jealousy. Using Maria's chest as a launching pad, I sprang off and gave chase - this was completely irresistible, the beast in question shot up one of the sprawling olive trees, and mewed piteously, and pleadingly at Maria.

"Daiii Agata" she called out to the cat. Meanwhile, I had set up my continuous yap yap routine, bouncing up and down under the olive tree and baring my teeth, hoping to look dangerous, and with serious intentions of grabbing that swishing tail in my jaws.

There were some things in a dog's life that demanded single minded concentration to the complete oblivion of all around you. Maria stomped over and picked the cat effortlessly out of the tree. At which point I spotted another, huge long-haired ginger and white mog, issuing from the darkness of its doorway, out into the light of the late afternoon sun, slowly ambling to a shaded plot, where it planned to rest- Hah! And another 2, involved in a mutual licking of faces contest.

“Mein Gott!” How many cats were there in this place? I chased hard, my pent-up energy of the previous 2 days confined in that sweaty little car, venting forcefully. I scattered the cats in a confused and most surprised series of squeals and meows, all, most satisfyingly, up the overgrown olives. I would show this shabby lot of moggies who commanded around here now!

Mamma C and the girls, evidently too exhausted to appreciate my success, or in fact to offer me any attention at all, were involved in the disembowelment of the mini. Cases, chests, laundry bags, brightly coloured rolling cases, helped by Stefano, in a stream of comings and goings, down the winding stone steps, through a patch of garden with the hugest fiercely spiked aloe vera plant, and in through a freshly white painted door to the left of the house.

This part of the house had all been whitewashed internally as well and gave the sensation of a sort of Greek island cave. It smelled strongly of fresh paint with just a hint of underlying mustiness and damp. Three camp beds, and one tiny, barred window, with no glass.

Our bedroom opened out to the kitchen, within the house; A terracotta tiled space with an industrially sized steel island, where Stefano, was stirring and uncovering a series of bubbling pots and saucepans - the most gorgeous and spicy smells covering the vague whiff of damp in our bedroom.

I trotted down amiably to keep him company, He was the cook, and therefore, the most important person in the house. I liked him very much and felt an immediate affinity with him. He was a dog man- I could tell, despite the presence of these pesky cats everywhere.

What a dear man, he placed an aluminium dish of some sort of unrecognisable but wholly odorously chosen scraps- sent from “la Nonna” apparently. As I started to wolf down the loaded dish, another black, and quite scrawny cat sidled up to me. The impudence!

In my unbridled outrage, I had left the dish for a second in which “Annina” the black subject in question, had snatched a chunk of my seasoned beef (or was it pork?) and stealthily leapt with ease up onto a high shelf above the television in the salotto - she was clever, this one- I would have to watch my back.

Mamma C poured a glass of red wine for herself and Stefano, and they chatted softly about the recipe he was preparing for their evening meal, while Maria and the girls laid the table out on the loggia. He was particularly passionate about Sicilian vegetable cooking, in this period, and with the wonderful local fresh and flavoursome crops, the girls reminisced how they often had a meal of crudites on arrival, (they came to stay here quite regularly - but usually flew EasyJet).

The wonderful little tender artichokes (Morellini) that starred in this dish were not in season now, and so he was preparing a version of “Caponata”.

He had 1/4 filled a wide and deep wok shaped pan, half with olive and half with peanut oil - ideal for frying quickly at high temperature.

2/3 glossy purple aubergines had been washed and cut, skin on. into cubes, excess moisture patted off with kitchen roll. In another large pan, 4 cloves of garlic, roughly chopped were sizzling and taking on a golden hue to which, some of his home-grown salted capers were added (the capers grew like weeds in summer, in the stone wall on the sunny side of the garden) and a few black olives. about 10 large peeled

and chopped tomatoes were then added, and once the tomatoes were cooked through, a sprinkling of roughly torn basil and dried oregano were added, finally a dash of salt and pepper, and the pan left to rest for a few minutes.
The aubergine cubes were then added to the oil pan, a few at a time, and as soon as golden brown all over, lifted out with a spatula, and dried in a kitchen paper lined bowl (to soak up the excess oil). once all of the cubes were cooked, another generous salting to them, and then left for 10 minutes to crisp up.
Then the sensual meeting of the 2, the tocchetti of aubergine gradually added to the enriched tomato sauce and warmed through for another 5 minutes or so. Served with a loaf of fresh Tuscan “lievitazione naturale” bread, for this was a far better option than the everyday and strangely stale tasting version of bread, typically from this region.
But, Stefano had prepared, as a most glorious start, to our weeks here in Italy, Mamma C’s favourite, large, perfectly ripened purple figs, gently twisted from the tree, just beyond the loggia, still warm from the day's sun on them , the thick but soft skins slightly broken, showing the scarlet red and intoxicatingly sweet fruit within.
A dish of these, with some finely sliced peppery prosciutto casalingo, signified all that was summer in Tuscany to

mamma C. I have to say that personally, the slim pickings of fat from the prosciutto, were far more favourable than the quarter of fig, offered me, but which I ate dutifully, showing my generations of breeding and superior canine education. More than I can say, for one in particular of the tribe of cats in and around this house. A certain Sofia, a ginger and white, adolescent of a cat. all muso and long legs, just past kittenhood, who, not content with jumping up onto the humans. dinner table, helped herself, stretching out in turns her esile paws to claw scraps of salami, almost encouraged by Maria.

I found it disgusting, and Mamma C didn't seem too impressed either. I would never beg or overstep the mark by stretching up on my hind legs to make my presence felt to Mamma C, at table, as I was wily enough to know she did not appreciate such open shows of dependence. Stefano also seemed disapproving.

The double act of Maria and Sofia continued, as the cat ,artfully hooked great mouthfuls of food for herself, whilst Maria shouting and squawking the latest catastrophes in Montespertoli, to the girls, who seemed both entranced , and a tad repelled at Sofia's soft white fur as it floated and landed on food and in glasses , and Maria's great globules of saliva and food, as her over enthusiasm in storytelling crushed her habitual lack of appetite.

I honestly did not know what to make of Maria, who although appeared to have a good heart; I could sense a lack of control, edging on wide eyed madness, that disquieted me, and urged me to keep watch for my beloved girls.

This woman was too unpredictable, and not to be trusted, albeit she made great shows of affection- there was something completely untamed about her. Stefano was much easier to read. A kind man, with much underlying humour to him, who loved on his terms. He was the strong and calming influence in this couple.

Following the delicious welcoming supper, as the sun, a great orb of melting deep orange leaked down into the wispy purpling clouds of the approaching night on the forested horizon. Stefano proposed an after-dinner party trick with Bill, a huge white cat with a ginger patch on his back, Stefano, on his feet, at a wise distance from the dinner table, opened his arms, forming a big O shape with his long arms in front of him, and the stupid cat, leapt through the hoop formed.

What a performance! and a paltry offering to my mind, despite the girls and Mamma C's shrieks of "Ancora. Ancora!" and their obvious amusement.

My accomplishments, formed through hours of patient training on Mine and Isabella's parts, trotting along park benches obediently, and through tunnels, rolling over and begging to the queen. I was a quick learner and had perfected many skills early on in my puppyhood, so I looked on from my position under Mamma C's chair, with a disparaging air at this ridiculous show of feline flamboyance.

The enormity of our voyage from Southeast England finally hit us, and with a huge wave of the greatest fatigue, the girls were just about capable of dragging themselves to the little whitewashed cave of a room that would be our base, for the next couple of months.

I settled, the relief at finally being on a bed, my paws outstretched at the end of Mamma C's rather creaky and rickety camp bed. Not the most peaceful of nights- as we were constantly disturbed by one or other of the cats, not used to having actual people staying in the room, as they insistently gained entrance through the tiny, barred window- blasted cats! Even that presumptuous creature, Annina, who deftly took position in the dark on the cushions next to Isabella- I was physically just too tired to chase her off, and so regretfully but exhaustedly left her to curl up on the white pillow.

Sharp shards of sunlight shone onto Sophia's dark tousled mane of hair, picking out the fairest highlights... I yawned and stretched lazily... then juddered in repugnance, what was that grotesque stink? a tirade of hoarse shouts and curses followed. “Che cazzo! Che schifo! Non è possibile!” Maria, with a canister of spray bleach was shooting the vile smelling liquid. hither and thither.

Mamma C, bleary eyed, went to discover, what was amiss. One of the numerous cat family, presumably ill, had squitted poopats all over the house. Eughhh! She stomped angrily, up and down in an ugly and worn green holey pajama, spraying and scrubbing as she went. My one thought to get OUT! this was truly unbearable, and I predicted a rocky stay, in the house with these mangy mogs.

The girls washed and dressed rapidly, being of a similar singular intention, and we set off for a breath-taking walk among the vineyards, the family deciding the plan of action. The girls would join their father, Babbo Vito, on the opposite side of the village, for a few days, maybe a week. He wanted to take them to the sea. Mamma C and I would go down to Florence today, to meet an old friend of Mamma C from her past life here in Florence.

At some point the mini would be "looked at " by a couple of Albanian mechanics, friends of Stefano and maria. We would use in the meantime, Stefano’s mothers ancient old blue Fiat 500 to travel around for the next few days. The priority today was to get away as quickly as possible from this screaming harpy. Maria- she was a force to be reckoned with- very bad tempered, and I thought well, to keep well out of her way. I did not trust her wheedling ways and terrifying mood swings.

Stefano had left very early, he was a chef in a nearby restaurant, and had to do all of the prep for the evenings' offerings there. He had given my head and ears a friendly scruffle and whispered softly in his deep husky voice, "A dopo, Cagnolino..." We followed soon after, squished together in the tiny fiat. Retracing our ascent of the previous evening, windows tightly shut despite the intensifying morning heat, against the rising hum of the tip, and across the village Piazza, down a long and narrow lane to a low redbrick house. A tall, tanned and bald, friendly looking man greeted us, well, principally the girls.

The deep lines around his eyes crinkled into an expression of pure joy, evidently very pleased to see his lovely daughters, and I felt the first pang of resentment to see them rush into his arms and hug him closely. They were mine! He was less pleased to see me. He feigned a shallow degree of happiness at being introduced, but I could tell immediately, he was not a man who had any affinity with animal kind. Perhaps his only pleasure was to eat them! He had a hesitancy and a reserve that I had learned not to trust in humans. I however resisted biting him in the bottom or the crutch, which was my usual reaction to such men (especially those bringing the post.)

Mamma C clutched each one of them, as though she may never see them again. I could tell, this was a painful parting for her. All of the ranting and harsh words between them in the car on the way there, laid aside, and forgotten. They remained there, with this man, on the little parapet of the house on the hill, waving us off, until we had disappeared from view, taking off, down the distinctly tortuous hill leading away from the house, and up the strada bianca leading to the main road.

The air smelled sweet, here at "Casa Lisi", Ginestra and wild jasmine floated at pleasant intervals on the breeze. Circled by cypresses, exhaling their musky, robust scent, giving a powerful undertone ...I was very much enjoying the sensual experience of this place hidden among the olive trees. And it was curious indeed, that I felt safer in this funny little car of Stefano's with the mushy brakes, than in the perilous and unpredictable mini.

Chapter Five: Meeting Mario…

So, we began our descent into Florence… Firenze… moving away from the sweet scents of Sophia and Isabella's family home, and as we did so, I picked up a very different smell- something quite feral - but nothing I recognised. "Cinghiale" ... Mamma C explained to me, Wild boar, this terrain was particularly noted for its dense preponderance of these yellow tusked beasts, dark brown, hoary skin- these animals could be very aggressive- especially if disturbed with their young. We would have to be very careful on our early morning walks, as it was exactly in those hours that they often enjoyed grazing in peace, rooting up bulbs of wild garlic and giaggioli that littered the fields here like small purple flags in springtime.

The local huntsmen would set out in gangs, from the 1st of September, when the hunting season officially began, out for days at a time, shooting to kill, and dragging the poor beasts, when cornered and shot, to their land rover trailers. They would then drive through the village to celebrate their catch of the day as blood-soaked lifeless trophies.

A few years previously, Mamma C explained to me, two contadino brothers and, evidently very poor shots, had

mistakenly targeted and killed one another on one of such hunting expeditions.
It was a story little publicised by the hunting community, as the threat of the animalisti and Italian hunting regulations, controlled by the green uniformed guardia forestiera, were frequently on the lookout to reduce the boar hunting groups, as it almost always amounted at least in this area, to far more than the “necessary” annual cull.
Mamma C drove cautiously, for her, on the narrow lane full of hairpin bends. down to San Michele a Torri, which had been a hotbed for the Italian partisans in WW2, and subsequently a battleground for the retreating Nazis, towards the end of the war, many of the buildings along the road still bore the brutal reminder of deep gunshot holes in their stuccoed facades. It was hard to imagine such cruel carnage in such a peaceful and rural village.
We passed "La tana del diavolo" a restaurant, that Mamma C had very fond memories of visiting in her late teens with her Aunt Yvonne, she wistfully told me - how they would take the bus up from searingly hot Florence on August evenings and come up here to the cooler hills to enjoy a meal, under the shade of the acacias.
Then, Scandicci, a typically ugly suburb of Florence, street after street of semi high rise blocks in varying shades of pale

yellow and terracotta, hurriedly thrown up in the 1960s and 70s, to house the former contadini, and immigrants from the south who moved u country in search of work. “Ad ognuno il diritto della casa” the social democratic hangover of many of the central and northern cities resulting in similarly unattractive suburbs to house the growing population of the time.

Mamma C informed me usefully, that we would be back the following week for “il Fierone” di Scandicci, a big country fair held in the wide avenues dividing up the quartiere.

From the huge population of dogs, I could see out with and without owners, I found this a little encouraging. We passed down through "Le Gore" in front of the magnificent country villa designed by Michelangelo for the Medici, My paws up on the dashboard. I took in every detail- and could just catch sight of, in the far-off distance, Brunelleschi's cupola, when a loud toot pre-announced the arrival up the hairpin bends of the number 12 bus, rampaging at speed, slowing for nobody, it swung perilously fast directly out into our path, taking a corner, and the soft brakes of the fiat 500 just halted us centimetres from its left-hand side.

Mamma C was relatively unflustered, and so I tried to echo her devil may care mood. We passed down through Galluzzo and a mingling of almost bitter, rich roasting smell of coffee beans from the bar centrale, with fruity wafts from the daily market in the piazza.

The roundabout at Porta Romana, with an especially hideous lumpen piece of modern marble sculpture regaling its centre.

My whiskers twitched. Passing down through a wide avenue lined with elm trees and poplars, translucent balls of seed filled the polluted air, and I sneezed loudly several times. We parked down on the road at San Frediano. A new concept for me, parking in the middle of the road, but again, Mamma C seemed unphased, clearly some other relic of her past life, and totally different from the ordered and controlled parking spaces back in Kent.

A warm breeze gently caressed my muzzle, as we trotted down the Lungarno, festering piles of undisturbed dog poo, to right and left, one had to be careful where one lay one's paws here. No poo bag or appropriate bin to dispose of in sight, here.

A fascinating passeggiata for me, however, frustrating for Mamma C, as I had to stop regularly to catch up on the news of this new and wonderful place.

A group of teenagers were smoking languidly, outside the huge stone embellished school entrance at the end of Piazza Frescobaldi, and they alternated between revving loudly their motorini, and calling out to a fat, fuzzy bearded, old lady, seated on the pavement surrounded by an array of plastic bags, filled with what looked and smelled like fetid old rags and blankets.

I stayed close to mamma C's legs. The pavements were crowded, and she seemed to know so many people here, and stopped frequently, embracing and hugging old friends, as we crossed over the river Arno.

She stopped to look in the tall windows of the bar at the end of Via della Vigna Nuova- shelves laden with brightly coloured marzipan fruits with frosted crystallised leaves.

Here the streets were much cleaner, no interesting piles of poo to investigate, all very clean and pristine. These were the streets that housed the finest of Florence, a city, historically famous for its trade and wealthy merchants. Gucci, Etro, Armani, Valentino and Ferragamo- all had their highly perfumed and opulent emporiums along this, via della vigna nuova and Via Tornabuoni.

The ancient stone pavements under my paws were warm and welcoming, several canine friends, in passing, all seemed very amiable and open to casual and intimate sniffing- most appealing! We headed straight into Piazza della repubblica and “Gilli”, mamma Cs favourite bar in Florence, where with a cioccolata calda at 15 years old, surrounded by the glitterati of the late 80s back then in Florence, under the shadow of the imposing bronze of the "rape of the sabine women" on the bar, she had decided, that this was where she would live.

The marbled floors were littered with delicious pastry crumbs, and I took advantage, snaffling up as much as I could.

"Ciao Bella"- another friend, Alex, Long term head waiter and maître D, there at Gilli. Mamma C and Alex had known one another for years, watched one another grow older, marry, have children, in Alex's case, see them marry too, and he showed mamma C photos on his phone of the newest grandchildren

As Mamma C savoured a perfectly formed cappuccino, I sat patiently under the table in the shade of the ivory parasol and wondered who were waiting for. I had been brushed and combed, my whiskers trimmed, and was sporting my new Barbour collar. Mamma C had an air of quiet confidence, not at all nervous, although I knew her as an expert at masking her emotions. The girls were pretty good at guessing her moods, but I am pretty sure I was the shrewdest at anticipating her every move- every whim and change of emotion- she could be volcanic at times, rarely- but when patience completely escaped her.

Although... I was not good at gauging her raising her voice - as a passionate person, she did this, sometimes with bursts of enthusiasm and laughter- sometimes in anger, mostly with herself- but what I found impossible to understand, were the emphatic positions in discussions she took, with many she had a close relationship with.

She laughed easily and frequently, her mood appearing to change, she was a complex but predominantly loving person. Kindness predominated... not weakness, but kindness, her soul empathetic and thoughtful- she abhorred all that was "bland" and monotonous or repetitive: so, my life was really quite a blast in comparison to many of my mates, and I loved her dearly, and thereby, offered her my most strong and virile protection. My teeth were sharp and honed. The orange vested postman at home, being my prime objective, he tortured me on a practically daily basis, invading my garden space and delivering all types of letters and packages. I had decided ALL visitors must be aggressively barked at, and possibly chased off.

But now, I sat meekly under the table, waiting, I was out of my home area, no familiar smells to comfort and reassure. She turned her head, and smiled widely, her eyes looked almost Chinese when she did this - and there he was, the object of her attention.

A Man, of medium height, and slim, jet-black ravens -wing hair streaked with white, a shock of it, his eyes, also black, brown, kind and a bit sad. His body betrayed an excited amusement, as he broadened his arms and embraced her warmly. Enough of that! I gave a warning growl, and he leaned down immediately, and let me sniff his hand, which smelt interestingly, very faintly, of horse and dog, smothered with eau de cologne, that made me sneeze.
"E questo, chi è?" duly introduced, I gauged he was a good man, and could see from his amused expression, he recognised my talents, as the perfect JRT ratter, and admired my physique. So, we could be comfortable with one another, and I settled amicably, back to resting under mamma Cs bare tanned legs.
Mario, for that was his name, following an initial hesitancy between them, sat opposite Mamma c, and took her hands softly in his. I had not seen mamma C so clearly happy and relaxed, in a very long time. They sipped on spumante wine, and speared enormous olives, whilst chatting and joking in Italian... I liked Mamma C when she spoke in Italian, she was more at home, and it suited her better as a language, for her personality- her emphatic gesticulating and wildly expressive storytelling fitted better with these people- the

English, usually finding her ways, at best confusing, and in general "over emotional".
A dish of fresh water, and a small silver tray of strange tasting treats, thoughtfully served to me by Alex- led me into a contented repose on my side, stretching my paws out.
The most enormous "BONG" filled the air, and I leapt up in shock and concern, what on gods' earth was this? "San Giovanni" explained mamma c, calming me, the huge bell in Giotto's campanile, announcing midday. She seemed full of joy at hearing its deafening proclamation- but really! What a truly terrible ground shaking noise! she was impossible to understand sometimes. "Ti ricordi?" Mario smilingly, and raising his eyebrows questioningly, asked. They had been lovers, and good friends many years ago. Soon after mamma C's move to Florence, following the impromptu death of her aunt.
Mario had been one of a crowd of twenty somethings, who would hang around mamma c and her Swedish crowd of girls. But Mario, was not one of the infamously named "pappagalli", though they had served their purpose as his friends, and barflies.
He had pursued her in quite an old-fashioned way, noticing her in the "GilIi" court of the time, when she lived in Porto San Giorgio for work, and would travel up by train for the

weekends, on visits to her aunt. He had sent her a rose to the hotel she always stayed in, the "Jennings Riccioli" on the Lungarno. With a simple note "speriamo che non si e appassito"- the rose was perfect, and the magic had worked. Mamma C, a sucker for romantic gestures, had noticed him too, and had accepted with alacrity his invitation for dinner, "Da Benvenuto" in via dei neri.

A passionate and enjoyable rapport ensued. She had subsequently moved into her aunt's apartment, in via dei fossi. He lived about five minutes away, in the medieval building above the straw market in piazza del porcellino.

They chuckled and chided one another over shared memories, some remembered in different ways. Sometimes, on the hotter days of midsummer, she would sunbathe naked, above the hubbub of the straw market, loving the secrecy and freedom of his rooftop terrace.

Occasionally, he would join her, for a naughty lunchtime rendezvous. They always dined out, at one or other of his favourite haunts around central Florence; Usually, to avoid his basic and most masculine of bathrooms, she would escape, dishevelled, back to her apartment, down the via Porta Rossa, after a night's entertainment and lovemaking, grabbing an early cappuccino in a tiny bar, halfway down.

A combination of events had led, after, just over a year, to their breakup. He was an esteemed younger partner in a ground-breaking architectural practice, travelling frequently to Germany on upcoming projects of modernising. She had become an executive in a fashion buying office, in Piazza Frescobaldi, quite unexpectedly, working for a huge American client, and had started travelling on a regular basis to America, New York and Columbus, and Hong Kong. Perhaps, it was their shared ambition to succeed, but in completely different fields. The depth of love originally shared- started waning, neither fascinated particularly in the others area of work., shared friendships unable to forge the augmenting gap in interest, they had started drifting. Then, the disastrous dinner with Mamma C's mother, over dinner at “Il Profeta”, which had practically sealed the end of the relationship for her.

Mario, completely unable to communicate to her mother, relied on Mamma C to translate for the entire evening, and had seriously disappointed and disillusioned Mamma C, with this complete dependence, being perceived by her, as a sort of weakness. She had, in some way, realised that, albeit far from home, and that decision being irreversible, she was not prepared, as yet to sever all ties with her family, back in England.

Subsequently, the love affair had ended. They had come together in the years following, neither one, capable of forming such a close and meaningful rapport with anyone else. Moments grasped in times of need, rare and beautiful: choosing Christmas trees together; hospital appointments; but the passionate love of that first honeymoon period, had waned and died. They were now, just old friends, sharing memories.

I glanced up, sensing regret and sadness, albeit their superficial flirting and affection for one another. Both softened with age, and at ease with their shared past, I felt sorry to see them grab one another, in a final clinch, their lives having taken different courses. A last meaningful gaze into one another's eyes, made me fidgety.

"Addio max", they rubbed against one another's cheeks, and smiled ruefully. Mario gave me a final back rub and with a "Forse ci rivedremo ... in un' altra vita...", they parted.

Mario left first, going to the bar, to settle the bill. Mamma C seemed to need a moment, I understood. He gave a last glance back, a half-smile, filled with sadness.

Mamma C straightened her sunglasses on her nose, cleared her throat, and softly jerked my lead "Andiamo Max". She waved to Alex, and we emerged from Gilli's Large terrace

to the pulsating heat of the early afternoon sun. Firenze, she told me, was always crowded, and always had been, from when she could remember- no tourist season as such, the only quieter months being November and February.
Being a country dog, and unused to such pavements, heaving with humanity; I was a bit jumpy and growled softly- there would be trouble if any human foot came within biting distance of my snout.
We dodged our way out of Piazza della Repubblica, and down towards the Ponte Vecchio, through the freshly tanned leather odours issuing from the tiny glove boutiques in PoR Santa Maria, and onto the bridge. We walked in the shade of the dark green and terracotta canopies, affording us welcome respite from the beating sun, but also saving from irreparable fading, the wonderfully stocked exclusive ateliers window displays of burnt orange velvets and ocean blue silks festooned with fountains of diamonds, pearls, rubies and emeralds, in the most sophisticated and unusual designs. No sign of any dog at all here- those that there were, closeted tightly in pink and fluffy bundles, clutched to their mistress' bosoms.
We turned left via San Frediano, amazing how the atmosphere changed radically here, the Oltrarno, where the less affluent artisans and tradespeople lived. Traditionally, the

houses were smaller and more tightly stacked at the sides of the narrow streets. An underlying whiff of medieval drains, always present, whether the forecast was for rain or not. The most delightful wafts of a garlicky meaty sugo, played around my nostrils and made my tummy grumble in anticipation, we passed the restaurant from whence it came, "Il cinghiale Bianco", Mamma C had been a regular there, in her single years, famous for their typically Tuscan "casalingo" cuisine, homely dishes like Pappa al pomodoro, made with stale bread soaked in tomatoes, Ribollita, a thick soup of cavolo nero, vegetables and beans.

"Ciao Bella". That familiar greeting ... the round-faced moustachioed owner, called out to Mamma C, "Bentornata!", she stopped to exchange pleasantries, and we moved on. Just a couple of doors further along, was "Camillo". Francesco, the owner there, not hesitating to greet, bowled straight over, a tall rangy man with extremely baggy eyes, he gripped Mamma C's shoulders in his strong hands, kissing her loudly on both cheeks, then bent immediately to rub my head, "Ma quanto tempo ?.." and they launched into an animated dialogue, of old friends in common, and people who had long since left the city and lost touch.. I hated it, when she did this- so utterly tedious for me, I searched for something interesting to explore.

The pavements here were spare of doggy faeces, as the restaurants disinfected with copious amounts of diluted bleach, the area in front of their various hostelries, every morning, on opening.

Seeing my plight, Francesco darted back into the entrance, and gave me a dried pigs ear- utterly delicious and very chewy, it kept me busy for the duration of their catch up.

Goodbye kisses and promises of keeping in touch, we crossed the road into Borgo San Frediano. Now here, a far more interesting prospect for a dog altogether. As the road narrowed substantially signs of dog waste littered the kerbs and tight pavements, and viscous liquids slowly ebbed between the uneven rough square cobbles of the street. Large metal dumpster bins, left gaping open with plastic bags that had been pecked or torn open, halted our progress, with me lunging towards the next exquisite pile of something indeterminate, at my level.

The smell was pungent and intense. As the road opened out onto Piazza del Carmine, a “Trippa” van was parked, 2 plasterers or decorators, judging by their attire. Leaned on its bancone, spilling glistening white chunks from their overfilled panini. I pulled on my lead, desperate for a taste of these delicious morsels, but Mamma c, equally determined, dragged me to the yeasty smelling “Forno”, where she bought a bag of schiacciatine loaded with salted green olives and a slice of stuffed focaccia. We arrived back at the car, a torrid inferno inside- left in the full sun of the day, and left Florence, with me panting for breath, and the setting sun reflecting aqueous glimmers of the Arno, behind us.

Tiny discs of rose and amber light in the air, as the heat of the day settled on the city in a wavering haze. We were leaving for the cooler climes of the hills, to my great relief, and the wide superstrada FIPILI stretched away in front of us, taking us gratefully there.

We banked up the steep slope, past the scuola elementare, where the girls had passed their formative years. We were meeting them at the bar Fiorentina, the hub of Montespertoli for aperitivi. No sign of them as yet, so we settled ourselves between the sprawling oversized leafy lemon trees, at a table. where I could easily spot their arrival.

Enrico, the barman, shambled his way over to us, in mid conversation with a couple of his football friends, smoking at the entrance to the bar. “Allora?” he smiled broadly and expectantly at Mamma C. “Che si dice?... le bambine?”

Although the girls were well past the "bambina" stage, they would probably always be referred to as such, by the ample group of montespertolesi. who had seen them grow up here.

Mamma C ordered an Aperol Spritz, that Enrico was especially adept at preparing. He brought the tall orange iced drink over with a selection of small plates, containing the standard perennially stale plain crisps, and an assortment of the leftover sandwiches of the day, cut into bite size chunks. Mamma c thoughtfully passed me down some morsels of mortadella and salami, when from around the corner, the girls accompanied by their father, arrived.

He gave Mamma C a dry whisper of a kiss on the cheek and took his leave. Having become a vegan, he no longer indulged in aperitivi. The girls had reddened cheeks and sprinkles of freckles, they hugged and kissed me, as though we had been gone for weeks. They had been to Forte dei Marmi, an elegant wide beach resort, about an hour away. It had been a favourite with them as a family for weekend breaks and days at the sea, and they always loved going back.

They ordered their favourite "chinotto" and drank down, gulpingly, hoovering the table clean of the aperitivo offerings. Babbo Vito, liked to keep their diet under control, as he was critical of their English style of eating. Mamma C and he exchanged a few pleasantries, a couple of air kisses, and he left them to their aperitivo.

“Dai sbrigatevi!” Mamma C must have spotted somebody she clearly did not want to chat with, so the girls downed their drinks, and I choked miserably on a dry chunk of salami, as I was dragged unceremoniously to my familiar space in the back of the car. we managed to squeal away, just in time, as a huge square of a woman, mostly bosom and the thickest monobrow I had ever seen, raised her thick hand in a disappointed salute.

I was feeling a tad bloated and my tummy rumbled in anticipation... I had to let rip ... such joyous relief. “Ohhh Max... che schifo!” Never good to keep air in one's tummy...and those Tuscan treats of cured meats, rather played havoc with my digestive system. Those added to the never ending tortuous narrow lanes we had to use to circumnavigate Montespertoli. I kept up a fairly constant stream of flatulence... beaten only by the appalling stench of the municipal discarica, as we passed, on our way back to Stefano and Marisa's., much to the girls' disgust and reproachful pleas for me to stop.

There was a strange, stilted atmosphere in the air, as we rounded the sharp turn, into the dirt track, leading to their home. I sensed having to pad on the most fragile of egg-shells, as we parked carefully in front of the white stuccoed church and set off on the path down to the house. Stefano met us with a distinctly depressed and resigned heaviness. He and Maria had just had an enormous bust- up, during which she kept up hurling a continuous stream of crockery at him, culminating in a royal Worcester casserole lid that narrowly missed his head.

At this point, he was beating a retreat, and was heading off to Beatrice, a girlfriend's agriturismo, away from this murderous environment.

He thoughtfully gave us the key to the door, where we could enter directly into our little whitewashed bedroom, thus avoiding a face to face with the insanely furious Maria, who, having downed an unhealthy amount of antidepressants, had passed out on the leather couch. Just as well, that we had all eaten our fill at the bar Fiorentina, as even had there, surprisingly, been anything to eat in the house, (Maria, almost never deigned the local co-op with her presence, always relying on Mamma C or Stefano to food shop) there was now no plate or bowl left, to eat them from!

Chapter Six: Nonna Carmela

It was easy to believe I was possibly in dog heaven, on waking to these wonderful Florentine dawns. At 5, the brilliant yellow orb of the sun, already resting on the hills, Mamma C and I strode out for a quick passeggiata, through the woods and over the fields of neighbouring Gustavo. Carefully avoiding his rather aggressive turkeys and geese, who spent much of their time, flapping wildly and chasing at astonishing speed, whatever or whomever strayed into their field of vision. Usually a very friendly man. Gustavo, following a recent spat with Maria, who had helped herself to the succulent peaches in his orchard. whilst on a brief trip up north, from which a huge argument had crescendoed, meant that on this morning, he but briefly smiled and shut himself in his stone clad kitchen, with none of his habitual jolly conversation.

In our haste to leave before Maria woke, I had left a few morsels in my bowl, which Annina swooped upon, ever vigilant and present around our company. She obviously recognised us as being the main providers of any food in the house, at least on our visit there.

Our faithful mini clubman had been brought back, with a new cylinder replaced in the engine, and We sped down the cypress lined avenue to Bar Silvano. the familiar shambling 1930s build, gorily painted in pink and yellow. Silvano greeted us with a tired air. Dressed in a pair of faded green overalls and a sweaty looking singlet, he wasn't the most glamorous specimen of Italian manhood I had experienced. But the bar... had everything, from warm and fragrant pastries, freshly cooked by his wife the same morning, to fresh fruit and veg, gathered from his “orto”. Strongly fragranced, cheeses and cured meats from a local farmer to a range of cigars and cigarettes, as well as the bar serving perfect espresso, cappuccino and aperitivi, he also stoked up the pizza oven over weekends and feast holidays, when the local community filled the rustic wooden tables nestling from the bar to the surrounding woodland.

Having consumed their colazioni, the girls and I, strutted arrogantly (well, the arrogant one, being myself) past the 2 chained Alsatians in Silvano’s front garden, at which predictably they set off on the most absurd and ferocious barking tirades. I insisted on relieving myself on one of the myrtle bushes, by the low stone wall, in front of their enclosure, which sent them into even more outrage, pulling so hard on their chains, they almost throttled themselves in fury.

I secretly held the hope that we would never actually meet, in their unchained state, roaming the estate, by night or very early morning. Annina, the feisty black cat, had been a survivor of one such attack, and bore the scars, in a ripped ear and deep claw tear along her back.

Aaaaah, so much more... well not exactly comfortable, but it felt homely, to be back in my old space under the front seat, my doggy odour pervading the carpet and spurious white hairs of mine, deeply entrenched in the black carpeting, testament to the more terrifying moments of our arriving journey.

As we built up speed, back on the Fipili superstrada, down to Florence, I settled myself back down, the deep rumble of the trucks hardly disturbing me as we smoothly streaked past.

Then we were on a bridge, again, which immediately made me nervous. This time, The Ponte dell Indiano, which crossed from Scandicci, on one side of Florence, to Peretola, the tiny and discreet airport, on the other side.: and a right old teetering affair it was. I could feel the heavy iron girdered monster shift slightly, as we waited in the traffic, plumes of exhaust and diesel filling the air. The volume of traffic, bottlenecking in its descent down to the airport. On either side, tightly planted vegetable allotments and orchards, thriving, unexpectedly, in the settling smog.

I settled into a light doze, the bottom of the car, warm under my full belly.
As I woke, I blinked sleepily at a square of whitewashed tower blocks, each around 5 or 6 floors in height, balconies, crazily stuffed with jungles of strongly scented white jasmine, and window boxes, pendulous with fierce orange and crimson pelargoniums and geraniums. Large leafy trees formed a circle of welcome shade around the edge of a dusty play park. Swings, slides, ropes and ladders, providing entertainment for the toddlers and children, whilst their parents and grandparents sat on the wooden benches, covered with carved inscriptions.
Nonna Carmela, (the girl's grandmother) a chuckle, playing on her lips, and her eyes creasing with joy, ventured out of the shade, and tightly hugged the girls, smothering their hair and cheeks with dry little kisses. She had the kindest face and warmest feeling about her- the purest of love, I felt. It was already mid-morning, and the heat was starting to build, so a swift trot around the park for me, a melancholy gaze at the ropes, where only a few years formerly, the girls had passed hours, with the local kids, and we were rattling up the building in the decrepit wooden, windowed elevator, to Nonna Carmela's apartment.

The most delicious of smells filled our nostrils, escaping from under Nonna's front door. The table laid; she had indeed prepared a banquet for our arrival. "Ecco a te, cagnolino..." -what a wonderful person- she had prepared a sumptuous overfull dish of roasted chicken wings and the finest beef slices, that I devoured, gratefully. A simple white platter with warm green figs, gathered from the tree growing in her balcony, and the saltiest of peppered Tuscan prosciutto, for mamma C, and for the girls, "Polpette della Nonna". Favourites indeed!

"Polpette", was an old recipe, perhaps dating back to the war years, when there was so little to eat. Patties of stale bread, softened in milk, and flavoured with much freshly grated fresh parmesan, and flat leaf parsley. Quickly deep fried in olive oil, and drained. These golden, emerald studded roundels of delight never lasted long on the table.

Her signature tray of the tenderest chicken roasted with garlic, bay and sage, and crunchy potatoes. Sparking with sprigs of rosemary, and the sweet small green peppers, again a Pugliese throwback, shallow fried at a very high heat, until almost burned, then exquisitely flavoured with chopped garlic, fresh mint leaves and a sprinkling of balsamic vinegar.

An hour or so, resting after this. I lay, prerogatively, in the centre of the sitting room on the cool white tiles, my paws stretched comfortably out. The girls settled to watch a disney channel favourite, they could only view in Italy, and had grown up with, meanwhile Nonna Carmela, took a dusty old shoebox from the top of the credenza, containing old photos of the family down south, that she and Mamma C pored over and giggled at. I caught sight of various sepia tinted teenagers and young men, with afro haircuts and long sideburns and high waisted trousers, from the sleepy angle of my watchful eye. Another sleepy afternoon passed with the darling Nonna, and with much kissing and hugging we trundled down in the elevator to meet the mini parked in the shade.

Back on the road again, we were on our way to Tavarnelle. The family had been invited to the 18th Birthday party of Matteo, a friend of the girls. A treasure hunt had been organised, and the girls fibrillated with excitement, at meeting up with some of their old friends.

Deep in olive oil country, this part of Tuscany: Matteo's aunt and uncle had organised a treasure hunt in their privately owned olive grove.

A small party greeted us as we parked up in front of the Aia (flagstone forecourt) in front of the sprawling sideways built cottage. Simone and Daniela, Matteo's parents, Stefano had also turned up with a miserable and overheated looking Maria.

Matteos' grandparents ,Sandra, Matteo's mother, who nodded over to us, and who was busy plaiting her daughter Silvia's hair into some intricate dreadlocks, replicating her own nest of tangled locks, and another group of Matteo's friends, some playing calcetto, in the next door field, some (mostly girls) limply bobbing around to tracks being played by a DJ , who had set himself up in the same field with his stage and lightshow.

The treasure hunt started almost immediately. I snuffled around, scenting the air full of warm roasted meats, which had been rapidly covered with tinfoil, more to cover from the flying insects, than to preserve heat from the still smoking barbecue, and Matteo (whose job it was, with his friends to dart from clue to clue. and accompanying tightly wrapped gifts.)

The excitement was intense, and I couldn't help but join them, yapping and barking with Rocco, their very friendly mastiff, as they raced in amongst the olives retrieving, brightly coloured sheets of paper with clues crudely scribed on them. They joked and shoved one another-eager to discover the final prize. A gleaming red and gold 120cc motorino, Matteo was visibly moved, a handsome blonde tanned boy, on the cusp of manhood. I could not quite understand the brink of tears moment as he embraced his Zii (relatives) thankfully...

The sinking sun smarted redly behind the olives, as the group moved to the trestle tables set up, groaning under the weight, the protections were gently removed from the wondrous mountains of food, when a sudden strong gust of evening breeze, lifted one of the larger tinfoil coverings, hoisting it from grasp, up and up to the eddies far above us. I, as were we all, was transfixed, the oversized silver sheet twisted and turned, dancing on the evening thermals, as if possessed.

"È un segno! È lui... è lui!!" Such an expression of joy that overrode the previous adolescent excitement, even. It was deemed to be Emanuele, Matteo's father, showing his presence at this most important moment of Matteo, his sons, life.

Emanuele had been killed in a terrible road accident, the summer before, and his loss was still deeply felt, by all who were there- we never saw where the bewitched silver foil fell: but the ensuing evening was enjoyed with a depth of emotion, difficult to describe.

The teenagers danced and embraced, the older ones, gripped by the emotion of “the sign” Emanuele had enacted, ate with renewed enthusiasm, as if invigorated by this ghostly demonstration of a man culled in his prime. Rocco and I enjoyed the spillings and shards of costata, reflecting and wondering on the strange sense of enchantment that dominated the evenings celebrations.

Chapter Seven: La festa del Vino

We woke late the following morning. Still slightly dazed, and in Mamma C's case, hung over from too much of the local Sangiovese, and a long chat covering spirituality and astronomy... amongst other subjects, with Stefano, lasting well into the early hours. It was when she decided to smoke one of his Toscano cigars, that I wearily decided to give up pleading for her to retire gracefully, and as soulfully as a mere dog can manage, I loped off and waited for her on the creaky camp bed.

Waking and rising so late, we had completely missed the "Tiro della Ruzzola"- an ancient tradition of Montespertoli, dating back a couple of hundred years, so it was told, but we were still in time for the all-important procession, that the village prepared for all year.

The "Tiro della Ruzzola" involved a group of the elders of the village (all men, logically), grouped together at the end of via Montelupo, at the furthest extreme of Montespertoli boundaries, which covered approximately a distance of 3 miles, to the village cemetery.

The road was closed, with "stivaloni'" the local policeman, blocking any entrance or exit, to the village, in his oversized biker boots. Neither he nor anyone Mamma C had asked

about it, could explain the rules, or indeed where it had originated. All anyone could ever tell you was that, on the same day of every year at the end of June, a select committee (most of them I recognised from the "Casa del popolo'" card playing gang, wrinkly and weathered, all of them) met and took turns in expertly throwing the "ruzzola", a large battered circular stone with a hole in the middle.
They shouted and jeered their way down via Montelupo, the "ruzzola" always ahead, and appeared to have the greatest of fun; possibly helped by the stealthily cached bardolesi of wine that 2 or 3 of them always carried for the group.
By the time they arrived at the games end, nobody really cared who had won, or indeed if anyone had won at all- and they were back in the bosom of the village, the lower piazza, ready to start on lunch.
We parked the car, riskily on a verge. The village was already buzzing with families and groups of friends, from surrounding villages and Florence itself.
As I jumped down onto the dry herby smelling grass, a tumultuous torrent of assorted smells greeted my sensitive nose. Large wheels of seasoned parmigiano, sweating their pungent perfume, on the mid-day air, the sharp gamey tang of goats' cheeses, wrapped in vine leaves...one delicious smell after another, the aniseedy sweet, burned smell of

“brigidini”, patatine fritte and “ficattole”, a sort of scrumptiously light and fluffy deep fried pizza dough.
I pulled at my lead in the direction of this most wonderful mescolanza of aromas. To our right the “Luna Park”, travelling fair, had arrived the previous evening., and was just grinding into action. Most frustratedly, Sophia had been spotted by a couple of old school friends, who insisted on stopping and chatting. I let them continue their awkward exchange for a few minutes, until I could stand it no more, and started whining, then in agonised frustration, yanked in the direction of the piazza. She seemed relieved to leave them... and we continued the steep lane up the piazza.
The girls had agreed to meet Federico and his little band of friends, later that evening at Luna Park. We needed to take our places in the piazza for the procession, which was due to begin in an hour or so. Passing through the pop-up market, we battled for space, in the growing crowds.
Stalls selling felted hair accessories and cheap leather handbags, “Vu Compra” turned market traders for the day, with their selection of African amulets, polished masks and musical instruments- then finally, the staggered stall after stall of local Tuscan delicacies that tortured my salivatory glands! Sheer heaven!

Mamma C, always generous in these situations, stemming as much from her own greedy pleasure, as that of buying from small and local farmers, stopped and tasted, Isabella kept me fed with tasters from each bancone of pistachio studded bologna, salted and rubbed hams, and we bought all manner of cheeses, jars of tiny sweet oniony bulbs in sweet, pickled vinegar, and apricot and plum preserves. She seemed to revel in setting up a lengthy and detailed discorso with most of the stall holders- thank God for Isabella!

A mounting sense of excitement and general hubbub of the undulating crowd, momentarily calmed and silenced by the shrill fischietto of the local police, pre-announced the beginning of this significant event on the montespertolese calendar.

The crowd hushed ...and waited, gobstopper large lollipops stuffed into the mouths of the smaller children, the locals gazed up the hill of Via Roma expectantly, to the old piazza, from where the deep and resounding roll of huge bass drums charged the still afternoon haze.

I felt momentarily paralysed with fear, as if perceived by some ancient calling, and sat bolt upright between Mamma C's shins, quivering- she leaned back to comfort me and scratch between my ears. I possibly had the best view from between the forest of bare legs. The drumming continued at a funereal pace, accompanied by a heavily discordant straggle of school age children, attempting some local traditional Tuscan anthem.

Grandparents gasped and tearfully kissed their forefingers in pride - then a vision - the most enormous and quite magnificent white bulls and heifers emerged from the top of the hill... Huge horns, hooves and tusks gold enamelled, sweet bouquets of meadow flowers, interspersed with barley stems and gold ribbons bedecked their gentle foreheads.

Guided by several roughly clothed farmers, they stamped and slipped their way down over the cobbled road, pulling a heavily laden cart with half of the village's children, dressed in yokels' attire. The crowd cheered enthusiastically.

I gazed at the gleaming white flanks, as the bulls mooed deeply and rebelliously. Sensing imminent disaster, I pulled on my lead for Mamma C to draw back, and thank the lord, she trusted my intuition on this occasion.

As the men struggled to hold the majestic animals back, their ebullience and restraint, coupled with the heightened and charged atmosphere of crowds cheering, drums booming and babies crying, two of the four magnificent beasts, as if encouraged by one another, let rip and with the noisiest farts I had ever heard, a stream of powerfully steaming

lumps and stinking brown liquid shot from under their swishing slimy tails.
The unremarkable effect on the crowd was an immediate and dangerous pulling back. Several of the front rowers who had pushed and elbowed their way there, now tried desperately to clean themselves of the fetid spatters, that had covered so many: and as quickly as they have pushed their way in, they shoved and pushed their way back, scattering baby buggies, disorientated grandparents and hysterical children in their wake.
For such an organised procession... the pandemonium was complete- few cleaner uppers had been foreseen in the programme, and did their best, spraying split sacks of sawdust, which did little or nothing to cover the gleaming piles of mostly liquid dung.
The little school band, eyes undeviatingly focussed on their music sheets, following the cart, and completely unaware of the blast from the bovine bowels, yet, sensing the apparent jubilation of the crowd, started slipping and falling in the malodorous mess, the "Fratelli D' Italia" anthem struck a discordant and disorganised end.
Mamma C was inexplicably in an attack of hilarity, creased over with laughter, as I pulled her back to safety. I was utterly shocked and had never seen such enormous piles of

animal excrement. My fear of human confusion prevented me from taking any exploratory and curious sniff of the stuff.
The girls had wisely and giggling, escaped to the chiosco selling "patatine and focacce" with Fiametta, Gaia and Agnese, old school friends, well away from the hot stinking scene, and I dragged Mamma C, almost helpless with streaming eyes, towards them, across the piazza.
My appetite, inexplicably encouraged by what I had witnessed, I was desperately hungry for a little something. Mamma C grabbed a welcome glass of the local Vinnovo, and I, snaffled most of Isabella's beautifully salted patatine. We formed an animated crowd with the girls' exhilarated companions, moving back through the market, and down towards the "Luna Park".
I slowed up, and, despite the thralling crowds of families and friends, few had brought their canine companions, so I was feeling tad bored, and longed for a bit of doggy banter. No sign of even a rogue to chase.
As we threaded our way through the upcoming throng, the smell and metallic, mechanical grinding announced.... The "brucomela", which had just started creaking into motion... a few laps to check the course, and they were open for business.

This old contraption had amused so many generations. An ancient rollercoaster fashioned as a giant maggot that passed through vertiginously high and swooping "tunnels' ' that were shining perforated apples. This time, however, the beringed and sleek-haired gypsy, running the ride, had decided the girls were too “big” - much to their disappointment... so, they were forced to explore and decide on the alternatives.
The “Takata”, had been decided- where I achingly watched Isabella, climb up into a huge doughnut shaped dancefloor, which with massively beating dance music, in an ever increasing crescendo to madness, encouraged the teenagers to dance, backflip and generally cavort…
As the floor rose on a huge metal stilt and the walls of the contraption started astonishingly spinning round, the floor suddenly, with no hint of warning, dropped. Isabella and her friends, screamed in glee and what I could only suppose was sheer terror. Flattened by centrifugal force of the spinning walls, their little faces contorted by the sheer speed, I whined in anguish... how could they subject themselves to such torture?
Mamma C laughed and pointed, and seemed not at all bothered, but could not placate my anxious whining state, so we moved away to where Sophia had again convened with

Fiametta and Agnese, and were climbing onto another ride, the “Miami Trip”.
It looked just a bit safer, but I was highly suspicious, and marvelled at Sophia's courage, and trust in the leering black eyed and golden toothed jabbering idiot who was taking tickets. He worried me.
Sophia sat, disguising her anxiety, gibbering nervously, as the man closed a huge protective plastic arm over each of her and her ride companions. The disco music rose to a deafening pitch, and the narrow stage they were seated on started lurching uncontrollably up, down, around and around. I could not bear to see her- the mixed screaming and... but was it laughing... or just sheer panic? she seemed in a trance, and I barked at the hideous monster of the machine, commanding it to stop... my barks unheard and amazingly... I seemed to amuse the other parents watching with contained amusement, their beloved babes as they were thrown around on this grotesque metal monster.
Mamma C, sensing my misery dragged me away, and in an effort to calm me, led me off to a pleasant and peaceful patch of dusty and comfortably doggy smelling grass, well away from the blasting disco confusion, under the encircling cedars, and I relieved myself thankfully ..

We wandered away from the Luna Park crowd, Mamma C, feeling my discomfort, and we drifted back with a few other stragglers to the wine drinking tent.
They joined Maria, fancy dressed, in theme with the day's events, quite improbably, as a buxom country wench. She was loudly flirting with a small crowd of locals from the casa del popolo, and a couple of uncomfortable looking foreign men, who, it was easy to ascertain, were most probably English or Dutch, judging from their sunburned noses and predictable white linen open shirts.
Maria bent over to kiss me on the top of my head, and shouted “MAAAAX... Gooood Boooy”, far too loudly, attempting futilely to attract their attention. Her wine drenched breath, mixed with halitosis, forced me to withdraw, repelled, between Mamma C’s calves. “E Che C'E’??” she loudly boomed. I retracted further- she was a loose cannon, once she had been boozing, and I had no intention of performing as her plaything to impress these lanky, but vaguely amused foreigners.
Undeterred, she grabbed hold of my lead from Mamma C’s loose grip and attempted to whisk me up into her arms. Completely taken off guard, I flailed and wriggled in her surprisingly strong hold, claws and teeth bared to save myself from this embarrassing and unconvincing show of

affection. As quickly as she had grasped me, she let me drop, in a twisting heap to the ground. Mamma C reclaimed me, angrily: But Maria, wailed loudly to her depleted masculine audience. “M'ha graffiato!! Guarda qui...” I had left her with a reddening wheal from a scratch on her exposed bosom, which only made the men snigger unsympathetically. She staggered off towards the nearby Farmacia, in hope of some more positive attention to her plight.

The slowly sinking sun bled its orange blaze across the horizon, behind the trees, and the low dusky pink and mustard stuccoed buildings around the piazza. An amber haze settled in shimmering bands of light, on the still, warm air. The enormous crashing of the contrasting music styles, calmed into a comforting and repetitive playlist of that summers' playlist of anthems and the evergreen favourites that represented Italian summertime, “sapore di sale”, “stessa spiaggia”. “Una rotonda sul mare”.

Songs that provided the soundtracks to generation after generation of Italian love stories and summer flings.

We waited, as the girls came up to join us, in a throng of adolescent excitement, fresh from their exploits in the Luna Park. Sophia, still visibly in shock, and trying desperately to hide it, and Isabella, buoyed up and exhilarated, as much from the Luna Park, as from some newfound attention from several of the boys from Sophia's year group, in her super tight ripped jeans, she batted her fake lashes, giggled and enjoyed this unexpected and pleasing reaction. A natural, her Italian heritage came to the fore, any former awkwardness dispelled.

A hurried exchange of numbers and snapchat accounts. Mamma C and I had purchased a bag of their remembered (from many after school treats) much loved filled schiacciatine from the bakery at the far side of the piazza, some with green olives, and others, especially for Isabella, with nutella. They fell on them voraciously, feeding the hunger from an animated afternoon of highly charged teenage excitement, with new and former friends.

The following day, Mamma C had planned to leave for the sea, having booked a log cabin, at a camping site, in a place down on the Tuscan coast, and Riotorto.

Chapter Eight: Mare - Riotorto

We rose at 5, with the first sunbeams rippling onto our beds. I had spent an irksome night, to say the least. Annina had hurled herself, in the early hours, from the tiny, barred window, that instead of discouraging the cats from entering and exiting freely, seemed to serve as a peculiar challenge to them.

A couple of the ginger moggies, left out for the night, had also risked their hides, acrobatically, and very noisily, knocking aside the chunks of wood that Maria had tirelessly placed, once again , to block them, and had met with the full force of my fury- tufts of fur flying in the air, and indignant barking on my part , mangled squeals and yowls on theirs- they had escaped into the neighbouring kitchen.

Most satisfying for me, I could not quite understand the family's disgruntled behaviour. I was purely and simply defending them, after all. Isabella kicked me off her bed, bleating about bites... from fleas that could supposedly, only come from me. could this be true? Surely that mange ridden mogs were the true culprits. I had been glorying in the most enlightening scratching episodes, the past day or two, and had put it down to the intense heat, that certainly made me sweaty and itchy, and my fur was also regrowing at an alarming rate.

In any case , up we were ,at 5, again ,carefully avoiding the happy grunting and loud snuffling of a mother wild boar and her young, at the entrance to Gustavo's wood, a quick rundown the cypress avenue , the sun already casting blinding shafts in the narrow gaps, and we crept, soft yet, stealthily back to the kitchen, where the girls were already breakfasting on fette biscottate and nutella, a pot of steaming coffee at the ready for mamma C's return. A bowl of tuna and rice for me.

More bitter complaints from both girls, of my appalling fishy breath, started our journey. Maria had slept over with friends from the festa del vino, who were taking her down to the sea to join us, and we would meet at the campeggio.

Stefano was staying home, to look after the cats, at least that was the excuse he stuck with, undoubtedly aided by Beatrice, and to continue preparing a series of artworks and sculptures he was preparing for a forthcoming exhibition.

The Fipili superstrada, this time, driving away from Florence for Livorno, was already busy, with early risen holidaymakers, heading, likewise to the coast.

We joined the inevitable queue at the tolls at Rosignano Solvay, gazing over to the stretch of glittering white beach to our right. A huge factory dominated the very far right of the view- producing bicarbonate of soda, with the same name - the beach, being the detritus of the finished product. Yet, observing the huge numbers of cars filing to park - it was obviously a huge draw, at least for the young and desperate to suntan in a day.

The girls lamented that this was where their friends were going today for the quick fix-bottles of beer and olive oil to rub into their "Pallid" skins, prepared for the deepest of bronze suntans in just a few torrid hours.

Having navigated past this block, we coasted freely, just a few motorists, heading for the beaches further down the coast. Umbrella pines lined the coast, with inviting glints of the emerald blue of the sea.

Mamma C's foot jammed harder on the accelerator in the anticipation of our arrival- the girls quoted names and memories identified with the exits from the superstrada... Castagneto Carducci... San Vincenzo... then, at last "La California" -most improbably named- this was our exit- we seemed to circle around endless roundabouts, and my breakfast sat uncomfortably high in my stomach, as I dug my claws into the carpet, grating on the metallic bottom underneath.

Our GB plates assisted the Italians behind, next to and in front, being just a little more patient than was usual for Italian drivers, as Mamma C, attempted to follow Maria's "easy" instructions on how to arrive. Only a few impatient and bad-tempered motorists cut us up and overtook us perilously.
A mess of untended fagus selvatica and acacia trees, almost covering the 1970s signage for "Camping al Fico", guaranteed our driving straight past, and waiting patiently at the lowered bar of the very smart, almost military looking next-door campsite. With a withering, patronising air- the voice purring out of the speakerphone, told us that we had gone wrong, and should take the turning, about 500 m avanti.
On considering the near dead juniper bushes, some half-hearted fencing, partially rusted and torn down, dividing us from the " smart" property. I could now understand the condescending air… A cloud of cannabis, carried on the wind, greeted us, as we parked up outside our very humble looking wood cabin. I could tell Mamma C was not impressed. Not really the type for proper "Bear Grylls" type camping, we at least had our own bathroom, thus avoiding queuing in our dressing gowns at dawn, for the limited communal lavatory block.

I loved it, unkempt trees and weeds sprouting everywhere, a darling little covered deck in front, where I marked this as our residence without delay. Plenty of seasoned doggy smells around, announcing a sociable time for me ahead. The girls unpacked the few necessities brought with us, and changed into bikinis and Hawaiians, demanding urgently, where was the beach?

Where was the beach?

Maria, with Clara and Margherita, other recently made friends, had turned up, with a motley collection of bicycles. A couple of vintage chopper-like, dangerous looking contraptions with broken seats. a grandmother rusted pink, with tiny, spoked wheels and a huge wicker basket on the front, and 2 ancient men's bikes with improbably high crossbars. This was how we would arrive at the beach. I could feel Mamma C fuming. She was not too keen on cycling, having a precarious sense of balance. I was to trot alongside on my extendible lead. The beach, they reliably informed us, was a "good" ten minutes bike ride, mostly cross country. Joy!

We tentatively cycled out through the rusted gap in the fence, the scratchy juniper bushes, catching on Mamma C's white linen Alberta Ferretti dress. She was not at all happy. Back onto the wider road of our arrival, where the traffic travelled at motorway speed, we navigated the wrong way up its one-way sense, the carefree bikini clad Italians, and the girls, way ahead of us, disappeared leaving just their tracks in the dust, for us to follow.

we struggled with a very loose and wobbly front wheel. The next step, a high fenced, on both sides, dirt track, with room for just one person, or bike, to pass: but naturally, the traffic was 2 way- with groups of teenage and older men, blasting their way through- heedless of our plight. Mamma C's bare tanned feet in her new Hawaiians, were coated in sandy dust and blood. It was at this juncture, that I felt the absolute and urgent need to evacuate my bowels and crouched accordingly.

Mamma C fumbled for a poo bag. I think she could heartily have killed me right then, but in her red and sweaty embarrassment, attempted to clear the squitty mess I had left. I was eager to get away from this narrow and impossibly busy passage and yanked on my lead to get us clear.

A bumpy and boulder ridden stretch followed, with a thickly planted field of sunflowers to our right, their golden heads, all turned respectfully to the sun at its peak- Mamma C accelerated vertiginously towards the inviting and resinous fragranced shade of the umbrella pines and gorse bushes that opened out onto a white sandy expanse, where she had to dismount, heavily pushing the bike, giving me the excited opportunity to sniff and mark my arrival to the "Nano Verde" beach bar. At last! Far more than the prescribed "10 minutes", and not a sign, obviously of our journey companions.

Sore feet and paws, plunged into the deep cigarette butt studded sand, we waded laboriously through the tree covered and tabled area surrounding the bar, to where we could see the girls' bikes, chained to a low piece of fencing, where Mamma C exhaustedly rammed the bike, nobody would steal this particular heap of rusted metal.

I could smell the salt on the breeze, and my lead, having been dropped for a fraction of a second, while Mamma C, jammed the bicycle, further into the mess of wrangled bikes. I, as if possessed, chased off to the softly roaring waves tumbling one after another, the whole prospect being far too inviting.

I joined the girls, laughing and diving like young porpoises into and over the waves. Wet slicked fur and hair, skin gleaming with salt crystals. Nothing could beat this fabulous release, we had been waiting all year for these cool, clear currents of the Mediterranean.

The sensual delight of the gentle warm and caressing massage of the successively white tipped surges and ripples, as we played and gambolled in its perfect azure swell.

"EHI !!" a crabby looking woman with her hair bound in a tired looking gingham bow, of inestimable age and a spider like body, all long, thin flaccid arms and legs, with an enormous belly, was catching the attention of Mamma C, who turned and smiled innocently, her hair golden and shining.
“Che schifo! Qui i cani non sono permessi!”. Dogs were not permitted on this beach.
Completely unexpected, Maria, perhaps had not known herself, she was not the brightest, and this, being a "free" beach, a spiaggia libera, rather than the traditional umbrella and sunbed decked expanses, she was used to, Mamma C had assumed wrongly, that... the rules were different here.
Well, there was nothing more we could do. The mood ruined, our hearts in in the soles of our feet and paws, we dragged ourselves heads high, dripping, but proud. Mamma C, determined to keep her aplomb, we emerged glorious, an ageing Venus and her faithful hound, out of the gorgeous waters.
Passing men with curly carpets of back hair, tiny babies having
their dirty bottoms washed in the shallows, and heavily oiled and creamed sweating trout pouted women gossiping on the bagnoasciuga - I couldn't help but wonder, why we were being shamed off the beach.

“Rules were rules”, 2 friendly coastguards, the spider woman had alerted us to our despicable crime, kindly explained. I licked the younger ones' leg, which tasted quite deliciously of coconut and grapefruit, he patted my head, and advised us that we would be “let off” of the usual fine of 200 euros, as we were “foreigners”, ignorant of the fierce laws, covering “free beaches”

We would dry off at the back of the beach, in the hot breeze, before attempting the journey back- and Mamma C would gird herself with a strong mojito from the bar. They sweetly indicated to Mamma C, where we could find a dog friendly beach- and thankfully it was far more than a bike ride away... though I loathed the car, the hostile environment created here, with unfriendly people all around, made me feel it had to be an improvement.

“Doggy beach” aptly named, (Italians do love to give the impression that English is a bit of a jokey slang, far from their superior and florabundant language), which we found hidden from decent family view, was a much smaller and murkier coloured sandy beach, a good half hour drive up the coast, with muddied rock pools abundant - no gentle tree coverage for shade, and very limited space for setting down your towels or teli to sunbathe, so a maximum of 2

or 3 hours in the torrid full sun, was as much as the girls, Mamma C or I could stand.
On the plus side, all breeds of dogkind were present there.
I romped in the waves , with a variety of hippy crossbreeds, timid huskies and limp legged Alsatians - to then return back, suitably exhausted and famished, to the cool shade of our deck, back at the cabin, where my afternoons were spent snoring gently, paws twitching, awaiting the return of my girls from the "Nano verde" beach and bar, as they wobbled and weaved their way back, suntans deepening, day by day.
Returning, as the sinking sun, spread its broad tendrils of deep orange and amber across the darkening sky, deep violet clouds and the "Cri Cri" of the crickets, silenced momentarily, as Mamma C and the adults, giggly and flirty, after several Mojitos, parked up their bikes, and ran to greet and embrace me, my simple happiness, contented by their effusive kisses, and a dinner of fishy pasta.
Our last, or what was to be, penultimate, day. We rose late as usual, Isabella in search of the perfect suntan, had made an appointment on the "Nano" beach, with one of the Somalian beach vendors, to have her hair plaited and beaded.
Maria and Clara passed by our cabin to collect her, and they cycled off, for their Saluto al sole, breakfast spliffs

wavering, as she naively followed them, complaining of the stink of what she pertained as some sort of pungent animal dung.

Sophia, more suspicious, and wary, decided to join Mamma C and I, complaining bitterly, she evidently felt she was in some way missing out, resignedly loaded the beach towels and hamper of food (mostly dog treats) in the back of the car. I settled myself into position, in the back, below the driving seat, and poised myself for arrival.

We sped off, the mini, so far behaving itself perfectly, and catapulted into the speed of the traffic on the A1 Road, overtaking the pensioners heading into "paese" for their daily shop, 2 etti di prosciutto, 4 slices of bread, 2 eggs etc- so tedious!

Almost missing the sharp right turn exit for doggy beach completely, we ended up behind a huge massey ferguson tractor, towing a muck filled trailer. Mamma C, a tad distracted, was evidently faintly irritated. Sophia commented on a spiralling, spindly column of grey smoke, that shifted hither and thither by the habitual morning breeze, and both tired and irascible, sunglasses askew, we joined the habitual mid-morning queue down to the beach.

A faint, but almost pleasant barbecuey smell smothered the air conditioning, as they opened the windows a fraction. I

darted my head up, alarm bells ringing wildly in my head, to see a column (at this point) of grey black smoke up ahead, blocked by the huge tractor and trail of diesel humming SUVs, ahead and behind us.
A field to our left. and way ahead, was burning. Nobody seemed in the least bit worried- everyone concentrated on the unique goal, of getting to the beach, and cooling our sweaty bodies in the glorious Med. The determination of reaching the beach, absolute.
Mamma C and Sophia seemed almost mesmerised by the rising glow of the burning field. Stark orange and gold, staggering and almost alluring, the fire greedily consumed all in its wake. The habitual conversational banter had ceased, between them. On the local Tuscan radio, Irene Grandi wailed “Bruci la città”.
The playful late morning breeze was taking hold, playful sparks shooting up into hot air. We continued to crawl, albeit cautiously ahead, behind the tractor, trapped by the cars following us, nose to tail. Surely the police or fire brigade would have been called and miraculously intervene. But ... no sign of any help. We watched, transfixed, our fate seemed almost sealed - I whined miserably, sensing disaster.

Sophia scratched my head, anxiously, and tried to appease me. Mamma C stuck her head out, of the window, and shouted to a soot covered contadina, on her way back to the main road “Ma - che succede ??” in a strangled squeal, as she watched in disbelief, as the shards of flame caught hold of two of the trees just ahead of us. Cars and SUVs, mostly and frighteningly behind us, in panic, rammed one another in 3 and more point turns, careless of the damage to their gleamingly beauteous automobiles, in desperation to escape.
The following seconds followed as if in slow motion.
The fire, fuelled by the sultry breeze, and the crisped dry crops, leapt to the opposite field- crackling, all-consuming flames, facetiously dared to stretch their darting tongues, under the belly of the mini. Sophia grabbed Mamma C’s arm, awakening her from what was almost a trance. “Mamma, Mamma! Fai qualcosa!”
She leapt into action, reversing madly, then throwing the car into first, and reversing again, we screamed away from the inferno-looking back, the tractor and line of remaining cars cloaked in a wall of dense choking black smoke and conquering, resplendent flames.

|In complete silence, we returned to “Il Fico”, as if hauling ourselves out of some sort of dreadful and repetitive nightmare. I felt as singed, and fire blazed as the poor mini.
The heat of the spontaneous fire had deeply shocked us all. With no appetite to attempt the alternative desultory bike ride to il Nano, Sophia and Mamma C, collapsed, deflated and stunned on their beds, and fell into a fitful sleep. I coiled myself tightly at Mamma C’s feet. Far too much adventure for one day.
On Isabella's group return, a spirited conversation on the lines of how Maria/Clara had successfully beaten down the price for her micro braiding and beading- I could sense mamma C’s disapproval -Ignoring her bluntly, Maria forged ahead , displaying some dull brown beach teli, boasting that she had paid far less than the going price that summer, preening herself in the mistaken belief that it was her “Fascino” and “furbizia”- only confirming her cheap market mentality.
None of them were very interested in hearing about our terrifying misadventure, and Mamma C, rather bored of the company, the groups' existence always based on the whereabouts of the next spliff, and their beach trivialities, decided, there and then, it was definitely time to move on.

We ate a rather frugal dinner, sharing a couple of cans of tuna, one of cannellini beans and a pack of multicolored strozzapreti, the top of the range from the onsite supermercato, that evidently did far more trade in tobacco and plant-based substances. The soot and taste of the fire was still fresh in our minds and mouths.

Chapter Nine: Mare – Castiglione

At 8 the next morning- a more leisurely start had been decided on, the mini looked war- beaten and tired- so it was fortunate that the drive from Riotorto to Castiglione, of just over an hour, was a relatively traffic and stress free one.
An ancient fortress with extensive and very lush, clearly well-tended gardens, rich green and dense vegetation, boasting tropical plants and trees, crowned the peak of this small coastal town.
The family chatted comfortably in the car, on the way down. Would Tiger Lily still be around? Isabella mused. She explained to me that Tiger Lily was a particularly beautiful and friendly dark ginger tabby cat with exotic oriental markings, who, for a couple of summers, had graced the gardens of the fortress.
Mamma C, Sophia and Isabella, had risen nearly every day of their holiday in the cottage at the top of the mount, to take her breakfast of fishy remains of the previous evenings' dinner- and they were well rewarded, as she was always there waiting for them, and would run to greet them, their offerings gratefully accepted, with many a lick, purr and satisfying stroking sessions.

My mane bristled in fierce anticipation, another bloody mog! This holiday has given me more than I could have imagined of cat company.
Well, I was here now, and would make sure no further miserable feline, however friendly and resplendently alluring would replace me in their affections. I made my feelings known by letting off silently... “Pooh Max!” Isabella squealed, disgustedly and we stopped the car, forcibly to let me out for a little leg stretch.
We had parked next to an acacia lined porticciolo, or Boat Marina.
The girls pointed out a couple of very fine yachts, one, all burnished wood, and polished brass, called “capperi e olive”. This had been their favourite, as young infants, when they would go fishing at the end of the molo, with their father, having first collected a small bag of squidgy pizza dough as bait, from the amiable Neapolitans who ran the pizzeria on the beach.
Their tastes were changing now they had grown up and they admired the Far larger almost matching pair of streamlined white and silver beauties, named “Bollicine e "Bollicine”, which they recognised as being part of the resplendent harem of a local millionaire, who had made his fortune in sparkling mineral water.

Having relieved myself on this charming passeggiata, I decided I would enjoy my stay here- lots of whiskery sea dogs trotting up and down, with a sense of belonging and distinct hospitality, and after many friendly exchanges of bottom sniffing, I really felt most at home already.
We left the mini in a huge and patchy old field, at the bottom of the town. This was the one and only disadvantage of Castiglione. Mamma C had booked a house they had already stayed in one summer, a few years ago, in Via dell' Amore, almost at its summit. The only vehicles permitted to pass through the arched entrance to the old town, were a fleet of tiny ape vans destined for cleaning the cobbled streets and collecting the rubbish on a daily basis. This meant a not indifferent hike, on foot, with whatever was being carried.
The girls lumbered sweatily with their wheeled cases and numerous bags. They joked about harnessing a trailer to me, but I was far too busy, meeting some more of the local canine community. A couple of glossy black and feathery spaniels, brothers, who lived in the bar at the bottom of the hill, the owner a baggy eyed young woman, who both sold her own particular brand of coffee, beans or ground, by a noisy machine, ejecting a heavenly rich aroma that wafted

in the air, and also, doubled up as a minuscule, but evidently very popular bar.
We passed a deep purply pink bougainvillea covered shrine to the Madonna, and staggered up over some seriously uneven cobbles, under the ancient stone arch, with a church to the left, I was kept busy, by several other dogs, all wandering free, and with enthusiastically wagging tails, who greeted my arrival.
I was very glad the girls had chosen this place to continue our beach holiday.
The house, in via dell' Amore, was a recently and finely modernised fisherman's cottage, and had exactly the right balance of sun and shade.
Not bothering to unpack, the family stripped off, gathered the necessary beach towels, hair and sun protection, and we set off for the sea, down the narrow-cobbled paths, and onto the corso, where one stretch of privately owned beach, followed another, the names evoking the promise of the inviting Mediterranean, Bagno Sirena, Bagno Nettuno, "Il Faro", each with fluttering brightly coloured ombrelloni and sturdy sunbeds.
Wonderful garlicky charged aromas, of the catch of the day, filled the warm air, from the numerous bars and restaurants.

We entered onto the wide avenue of the lungomare, and into the packed bar of "Bagno Balena".
Mamma C hugged and kissed her old friends, Licia and Franco, the owners of this stretch of the beach. He was a clam fisherman, when not in the beach season, and she, a schoolteacher at the local liceo in Grosseto.
Checco, their younger son, who also doubled up as PR for the local discotheque on the neighbouring hill "La Capannina" and was one of the most desired and admired young Italians on the entire beach.
He languidly, but with a natural charm, accompanied us to our ombrellone, and casually invited me, with the girls, to a game at sundown, with his brothers' 2 fox terriers of beach volley.
We leapt and frolicked, they back kicked and punched up. The girls had both played volleyball, when at school in Italy, and were overjoyed at a game after so long... a couple of hours of exhaustive play, and a sudden hunger kicked in. Desperate for some fresh fish, we decided to wander along to the fisherman's Banconi, further down the molo, and see what was available today. Mamma C decided upon a red mullet, fresh and glistening, and cooked "All' Isolana" up at the house, on a bed of finely sliced potatoes and red

onions, a couple of cloves of garlic and some sweet cherry tomatoes, was just the perfect end to our day.

I lay at the cottage entrance, on the warm cobbles, enjoying gnawing the carcass in the late evening sun, growling at passing friends who attempted to get a sniff. But no need, the dogs here were well fed, and purely showing their amiable interest in my repast.

Castiglione was famous for its dangerous cross currents, and each "Bagno" had at least two or three lifeguards.

In the morning, the sea was a veritable millpond, calm and crystalline. This was generally when the old folks and their grandchildren would walk in the shallows and build sandcastles. But encouraged by a fresh and rumbustious Mistral breeze, by mid-day there were almost always sizable foaming waves, crashing onto the beach from both left and right.

The families returned to their beach homes for lunch and a riposino, at this hour. Famous for these rolling breakers, Castiglione boasted a multi-aged surfing community, as well as courageous and lifesaving dogs, who were regularly exercised at lunchtime.

One of these, Teseo, became a particular friend of mine. A 5-year-old strong golden labrador, he would come down to the beach, next door, "La Vela", which was historically an old haunt for the local fishermen to come and drink and tell their stories.

Punctually, at midday, with his walnut brown honed muscle of a trainer, Teseo would dismount from the crossbar of his masters, motorino in front of the bar: and before he was dutifully harnessed up, he and I would race one another through the ombrelloni, skimming the ardent sand, to plunge into the roaring blue of the Med.

Paddling energetically, our wet heads rising majestically above the dips and foam tipped rises of the rocky sea. Sometimes the girls would join us, gripping onto Teseo's harness, he thrust his strong barrel chest forward, paws pacing the water confidently, dragging their limp bodies to the shore, he then delivered them, with impeccable professionalism, giggling onto the hot sand, and they thanked him, showering his wet flanks with kisses.

The days ran, seamlessly, into one another, sun and happiness -filled. The belltower, at the hilltop church, with its heavy iron bell announcing the start of the day chiming 7 times. Sophia and Isabella had scampered up there, with me, in hot pursuit. Mamma C kept me on a tight lead, to search out Tiger Lily, but there was, sadly, for them, no sign of her. I gobbled the scraps of fish they had prepared for her, in the lack of any evidence of her existence at all.

One evening, we were invited for a sumptuous dinner of deep fried pesciolini, and pasta alle sarde (Sicilian style) at Rocco and Marys', other old summertime, and beach friends, at their cottage behind the lungomare.

I particularly took to Mary, with her periwinkle blue eyes, as she slipped me luscious titbits from the table.

Another day, we rose at 6, to take the old white ferry boat to explore the nearby islands of Giglio and Giannutri. The girls and I took advantage of the wide expanse of azure glimmering sea, to dive into the sea and swim around "Le formiche", a couple of the smallest flowered islands, at the halfway point between Castiglione and the island of Giglio.

Yet another evening, was spent "Nel Buco", a quaint, tucked away trattoria that seemed carved into the fabric of the hill, right at the top of the old town, where Gigi, the owner entertained us with his preambolo of tasters, and sang lewd Tuscan ballads, accompanied by the yodeling waiters' guitar.

This year, we had been lucky to avoid the customary and unpleasant arrival of the treacherous weaver fish, lurking under the sand, or the Portuguese Men O War, pulsating purple bulbous heads of jellyfish with miraculously long and potentially lethal tentacle like streamers, flowing widely behind them.

The girls, blithe but melancholy, recounted their various encounters, over the years, as we drove away from Castiglione, having sadly said goodbye to the old and new friends made, and our dear little cottage in Via dell' Amore. My fur was still stiff with salt, from the last morning swim, I stretched comfortably into position,

Where were we off to now?

Chapter Ten: Monte Amiata - Abbadia

Riccardo, Barbara and Giovanni had been friends of the family since the girls had started school together at the friendly convent school in Tavarnuzze, run by the suore salesiane, nuns. The mini clubman, having been well rested in our time at Castiglione, was in fine form, and we chuntered along smoothly, the girls looking forward to meeting up again. It had been a few years.

We had been invited to stay over, for the festa di San Lorenzo, where it had been planned, we would stay up all night, and watch the night sky. Abbadia, and their house situated right at the pinnacle, did not qualify as a mountain, but was one of the highest points in Tuscany, and being scarcely populated by human light sources, we stood an excellent chance to spot shooting stars.

We passed from the sun bleached blue and white seascape to to the rich ruddy brown of the Sienese earth in the recently ploughed fields. Dark jewel green leaves on the mulberry and acacia trees, the colours intensified by the clarity of the air up here. Following long and straight roman roads, on what had been a part of the via cassia. Barbara's

directions had been abundantly clear and precise, A librarian by profession, she was by nature quite methodical.
She greeted us warmly, “Maaax” she let me jump up at her, licking her face. The family had stayed with us a couple of years ago, and I was overjoyed at seeing her again. Her face creased into a huge smile, and she hugged the girls affectionately. Mamma Cand she had a friendship, that went beyond words, a level of understanding, and their eyes creased in humour at unspoken jokes they shared.
She had prepared a delicious fragrant panzanella for lunch, Tuscan bread soaked in watered down wine vinegar, paper thin slices of pungent red onion and cucumber, bold black olives, tiny sharp yet sweet capers and the plumpest occhio di bue tomatoes, all from their vegetable garden.
Mamma C relaxing, let me off the lead, and I shot off, energised by this fresher sharper air to do a few laps of the enormous sloping meadows, stretching both behind and to the side of the house.
An array of various sized old metal pots (This was Riccardo’s parents’ country house- and so she dared not use the newer additions to the kitchen) had been prepared, for the children to go blackberrying after lunch. The borders of the meadows were thicketed with a colourful tapestry of Laurus

nobilis, juniper, gorse and of course, huge mounds of brambles, heavy with juicy blackberries.

The teenagers, having overcome their original embarrassment and awkwardness, now slipped back into their former comfortable companionship, and set off, banging their metal pans, happily bickering and retracing old memories in common, of the afternoons spent at Le suore, as young infants, when they should have been sleeping, but got up to all kinds of mischief.

I scampered, companionably, next to them, sometimes behind. enjoying the sensation of the wild grasses against my muzzle. I could scent rabbits... and hare... and even foxes.

I would wait until evening, when they ventured out of their lairs to give them a good chase!

We returned triumphant. Mouths stained a dark purple with how many the children had gorged. Even I had tasted some of these extraordinarily large and seedy fruits that had been tossed for me to catch. And after a light salad of pecorino and pere, the setting of the scene was being prepared.

I sensed an air of excitement for this forthcoming "Notte delle stelle cadenti"

Comfortable armchairs and deep plush cushions were dragged out of the salotto, and into the meadow. A deep fragrant scent of a thousand flowers as they closed their

petals with the approaching evening. A few bottles of beer, and coarse picnic plaids, for the temperatures plummeted here, and a cloud free night fell amazingly quickly upon us. Giovanni was the first to spot one. We had barely taken our places- organising the angle of recline on the chairs to get the best and widest view of the deep velvet sky and its agglomeration of sparkling diamonds. I lay patiently on the warm grass, ants tickling my belly pleasantly. “IMPOSSIBILE!” exclaimed Riccardo, ever the professor. It was barely dusk, yet... the lightshow had already begun...
Riccardo and Giovanni had an ongoing competitive banter. “Nooooo ... era un satellite” Never before had we noticed the bright spots of light in the inky black sky, as they followed on a set projectory - not to be confused with shooting stars, however. Gio was indignant that he had seen one, and therefore had been the first!
As the sky rapidly darkened in tone and seemed indeed to fold protectively around us like a deep blue-black mantle. The stars far more intense in their glowy candescence. They were easy to pick off - shooting away explosively- but in fractions of a second, it was both exciting and extraordinary- I had never witnessed such a spettacolo. Both the adults and the children, heads inclined backwards, staring intently upwards - joyfully exclaimed as they spotted these

darting beads of light. Giovanni and Sophia spotted them continuously- Isabella chose another area of sky to stare at. Even the wild animals were transfixed by his mesmerising sight. The habitual calls of the odd vixen, or the native caprioli calling softly to one another, were silent tonight. The atmosphere seemed charged with an uncommon spiritual tension. The adults exchanged experiences of where they had first seen their first Notte di San Lorenzo. For Mamma C it had been on the beach at San Miguel in Ibiza. As a precocious teenager, she and Zio David, not sure if it was the potent beach bar punch, or reality, had watched, bewitched as the sky had lit up with falling stars.

The only sound, the persistent whirring and clicking of the crickets, which gradually subsided into a taught silence, as the temperature dropped.

I curled myself into a tight ball, the ants had receded, back to their tunnels deep underground. It was past midnight and the exhilarated, but now tired family group decided to retire to their beds, perhaps, just perhaps, the best of this incredible natural shower of shooting stars had peaked.

The subsequent days could not hope to compete with that night. But the group established a contented group, with routines of daily walks- showing me hidden knots of woodland, where I could scamper freely, drinking up the new and curious truffly odours under the ancient oaks. Trips to visit the churches of Abbadia and Montalcino, while I waited under shadowy trees, befriending passing canine acquaintances. Early merende and lunches of locally formed cheeses, salted hams and salamis and plump green figs (of course!) warmed in the sun. Long afternoons passed, dozing in the sun with the cicale chirruping loudly in the olives and the Oaks.

The final few days of relaxed happiness, and then it was time to make our final stop back at Montespertoli, to pick up the rest of our luggage, and head back to our new home in East Sussex.

Emotional addios, and promises to return in the late Autumn, for sweet chestnuts to roast and savour with the local vino Novello. Sophia gave me a last swoosh down with the garden hose and rubbed my coat with verbena essence in preparation for the long journey ahead.

Stefano had baked us a torta rustica, with salty ricotta and sundried tomatoes for the trip, Maria was away on a rare trip, with friends: and for the last time set off down the strada bianca, passing Bar Silvano and the humming discarica, the vineyards groaning with ripening fruit, and the silvery tousled olive groves.

Chapter Eleven: Return to Blighty

On our return to Botinaccio, and Montespertoli, Stefano had baked us a torta rustica, with salty ricotta and sundried tomatoes for the trip back and bade us a hasty goodbye. Neither he nor Maria were fond of farewells.

Maria was away on a rare trip, with friends: but had kindly left me with a gift of a cooling gel padded cushion.

For the last time, we set off down the strada bianca, passing Bar Silvano and the humming discarica, the vineyards groaning with ripening fruit, and the silvery tousled olive groves covered with green budding fruits. The Girls were temporarily silenced, partially by a sudden sadness at our partenza, and a heavy dread at the imminent voyage ahead of us.

This time, Isabella sat next to Mamma C up front, Sophia finding it far too stressful, following the heated exchanges on the Morandi bridge in Genova, on our arrival 6 weeks back.

The family were in a sad and reflective mood, as befitted the end of any holiday: but for them it always signified a more poignant journey - remembering their initial escape from the horrendous break up of their family, several years before.

The battered blue little Peugeot 6, complete with the family cats in cages, and as much as they could fit into the limited space remaining.

That had been an escape to what they had hoped to a better life and fresh start in England.

I dozed peacefully on my cool gel cushion and relished the relative silence of the first few hours travelling up through Italy, punctuated only by coffee stops for Mamma C and pipi' stops for me.

Somewhere close to Torino, our last Italian stop, that strange shard of rock I had seen, on our way down, a partially forested fragment of mountain, in the otherwise flat Alessandrian landscape. It looked like a discarded piece of Mount Olympus, torn asunder and discarcarded by Zeus himself… We would soon be in Switzerland.

The amount of traffic, as we approached the San Bernardo tunnel, was bewildering. AS usual - the best made plans... Mamma C had thought to cross the country (Switzerland), in a couple of hours, but it was clearly not going to be such a rapid and stress-free traverse on the otherwise and habitually, clinically organised Swiss autoroutes.

In addition to the unbeknownst return to school the following day for Swiss schoolchildren: there had been a fatal accident in the tunnel.

Hence a temporary traffic light, allowing just 5 vehicles through at a time to the tunnel. So, we sat, tension building, in the lines of smoking and fuming trucks and cars, waiting our turn. Rihanna and DJ Khaled on the Skyrock radio channel, that was the only one we could tune properly, that the girls had laughingly rejoiced as this summer's anthem, now only served to pall and irritate further, our static situation. Mamma C also had an anxious eye on the ever-rising temperature of the mini's engine.

After several, perhaps 3 hours, we finally made it into the tunnel out of Italy, Mamma C was visibly rattled and kept her eyes fixed on the route through.

Her arms stiff as she gripped the steering wheel, I could feel her nerves palpably., as we kept up the steady obligatory 50 kph in what seemed this endless scarcely lit aperture through the mountain, dividing the countries.

The Swiss autoroute, no less crowded, gave us no chance to stop for relief or coffee… we had to find the exit into France, and now the crepuscolo hour had arrived, and concentration was considerably waning.

Mamma C overtook great convoys of trucks at a time, attempting to gain some of the time lost in the tedious wait for the tunnel. We had already been over 6 hours on the Swiss leg of the journey, when we horrifyingly realised, we

were heading with the many German plated trucks up to their beloved homeland. GERMANIA!
We had completely missed the exit for Lausanne. Almost at the same moment, all of the family's' mobile phone network went down. In near desperation, to get off of the crazily overcrowded autoroute, we misguidedly shot off at the nearest exit
Seriously uncomfortable, all of us, we stopped at an improbable petrol station, somewhere in the dark hills above Berne, as the mini was also on its last legs, and I had the longest pee ever; Sophia tried to drag me away from the miserable little bush I had sought out in the gloom, but I persisted in finishing, my sense of consolation, complete. Even if my nerves were frazzled by this heightening tension, of our being completely lost up in the Bernese Mountain range.
Faced with a series of weblike interlinking narrow roads, we climbed ever further upwards in the already fatigued mini, passing village after village, in the scantily lemon seed lit tracks, with scarce directions of anywhere at all recognisable, and not a soul on the roads.
At one point, Sophia spotted someone in a lavanderia, in the depressing misty gloom and insisted on Mamma C

stopping. She courageously ran in and attempted in her best French; she asked the woman if she could direct us to Dijon. "DIJON?" the woman excitedly responded, "is at least 5 hours away!" Dijon, where we had a warm and comfortable Ibis hotel booked, on the peripheries, for our overnight stay. That was the point where exhaustion hit Mamma C. The 16 hours behind the wheel was just too much, she pulled in at a grassy verge, and smashed her head down, in complete defeat.

Taking a deep breath, she rose up, and opening the door for me to trot around and find a suitable clump for a well needed dump, stretched her own legs in painful repose.

It was about 11 in the evening, and just one faint light in one of the pretty painted cottages waned. As she stretched out against the car, a shawled lady holding a torch came out of the cottage. It was Laure Dumont, our saviour for that evening. She invited us into her small and cosy back room and showed us a map of the way down to Dijon.

Mamma C, in her dog-tired French, explained our plight. They spoke softly, to avoid waking Laure's husband. As if in a dream, Laure told them she was preparing a gite for opening, the next summer, no hot water, but a bedroom ready and made up for relatives who would arrive the following week. We could sleep there. Patchwork quilts and large feather eiderdowns, at this point, it looked like heaven and we collapsed gratefully into the dimly lit huge bedroom.

I woke, with a gentle clanging of cowbells, Mamma C opened the window a tad, to glance through the dense early morning mist,

A succession of beautiful russet brown, black eyed cows, were pacing their way carefully but knowledgeably, down the narrow track, peeling off to left and right, each one heading back to their personal home farm. Unassisted by any human presence, these magnificent creatures, having grazed in the pastures higher up the mountain, were returning home.

I growled softly, not a sight I had ever witnessed, and was suspicious. Cows in England were quite an aggressive lot, from my experience. This was another breed of bovine, calmly and intelligently following their homing instincts. It was a miraculous sight, in this almost ethereal weakly sunlit mist of early morning.

Near freezing showers, and a plate of hot croissants to see us off, before her husband awoke, a warm embrace and "Bon voyage" from Laure, we mounted in the mini, once again, refreshed and energised from albeit a brief night's rest. Still a bit in disbelief at our amazingly good luck, at finding such a kind soul, we took the road leading down from somewhere near Neuchatel, passing through classically pretty and pristine blanched white and red shuttered housed villages, to take the main autoroute taking us back through Dijon and on to Calais.

The unrepentantly dull drag up to Calais, uneventful, thankfully, save the occasional pit stop for petrol, coffee, sandwiches, and the obvious necessaries. The French autoroutes are so much more relaxing than the Italian autostradas. The girls and I slept deeply. Me, on my warmed by sheer body heat gel cushion, Isabella slumped exhaustively over the lumpy bundles of baggage on the seat next to her, and Sophia, head back, and lolling uncomfortably.

By early evening, we arrived at Les pas de Calais. Isabella, responsible for doing a quick check of the documents to get through the border control, suddenly and dreadingly exclaimed, waking us all into a state of panic.

“Mamma! Non c'è Max sul biglietto!” Somehow Mamma C, in all of her organisational skills, had lacked to include me on the Eurostar return ticket.

Mamma C had to decide immediately what to do.

Decided, I must travel “clandestine”, undeclared and, more importantly, unobserved by the officials.

Isabella, with a few "pigs in blankets" treats, succeeded in administering me some drops of a calming, immensely strong sedative, that they had used previously with the cats, years previously, (and which had almost finished Tabbi off the prescribed dose not having been observed in Mamma C's panic)

A sedative available by vets' release, only in Italy, and probably completely illegal in the UK. My eyelids drooped heavily, and I sank into a weird state of trance like sleep, dogs I had befriended that summer rolled around my head mooing, and dark eyed cows barking strange commands that I couldn't quite understand.

Mamma C drove slowly and determinedly through the PETS reception area, guilt weighing heavily, but she smiled confidently... Isabella covered me carefully with a plaid blanket, completely covering me from view.

A very immediate sense of hunger and desperate need to discover my surroundings, however, superseded the drugged effect, and I popped my head up, on the point of passing the French controls, sluggishly but forcibly.

Isabella fell on top of me, and the French official, checking our documents, seemed not to have noticed me, but curiously, and officiously invited us to join the queue of cars, to one side, for terrorism checks. An estate car with a family of what looked like Nigerians in front, and behind, a jeepload of Somali looking youths.

An anti-terrorism black uniformed official, then insisted that Mamma C open all of the car windows and proceeded with what appeared to be a flashing electronic oversized tennis racquet, that emitted a series of bleeps and squeaks, that fortunately due to my drugged state, I was unable to respond with my habitual warning growl.

He passed the device in and over the car, then instructed us to pass through a heat sensored arch, at walking pace in the mini.

With bated breath, Mamma C and Sophia, blanched with fear,

Isabella lounged convincingly over my tartan plaid, smiled innocently.

Nothing - no alarm, no blaring device screaming for us to halt. I wondered in my muzzy state, maybe I was indeed dead? I relaxed down under the thick woollen blanket that Isabella was crushingly covering me with and fell into another deep and drugged collapse.

My head, banging and woozy and, but clearly awake and still, apparently in this worldly existence, I managed to grapple the felted blanket aside with my scratching paws.

We were, once again, comfortably on the beach road heading towards Hythe.
"Maax! we made it!" Isabella laughing, hugged me, with the greatest joy, and I felt beloved and adored. She fed me some well-deserved, strange bison treats.
Folkestone was behind us, my wicker basket with its cool cotton cushion awaited me in our new Sussex home.
I would stretch out and sleep…. at least a week.

Fine

europe
books